ARML – NYSML Contests
1989–1994

The Contests in Mathematics Series

Editorial Board

Titles in this series:
1. Dmitry Fomin and Alexey Kirichenko, *Leningrad Mathematical Olympiads 1987–1991*
2. Lawrence Zimmerman and Gilbert Kessler, *ARML-NYSML Contests 1989–1994*

MathPro Press books can be ordered from:
MathPro Press
P.O. Box 388
Ashland, OH 44805 USA
Phone orders: (800) 247-6553 or +1 419-281-1802 (international).
Online orders: http://www.MathProPress.com

ARML – NYSML CONTESTS 1989–1994

Lawrence Zimmerman
Gilbert Kessler

MathPro Press

Westford, Massachusetts, USA

Contests in Mathematics, Volume 2

Mathpro Press
P.O. Box 388
Ashland, OH 44805
USA
e-mail: stan@MathProPress.com
online: www.MathProPress.com

1991 Mathematics Subject Classification: Primary 00A07

Publisher's Cataloging-in-Publication Data   **AACR2**

Main entry under title: ARML–NYSML Contests 1989–1994
/ by Lawrence Zimmerman and Gilbert Kessler
— Westford, MA : MathPro, 1995
xviii, 190 p. ; 22 cm. — (Contests in Mathematics; v. 2)
Includes index.
 1. Mathematics Contests — United States
 2. Mathematics — Problems, exercises, etc.
I. Zimmerman, Lawerence J., 1946-
II. Kessler, Gilbert W., 1936- III. Series.
QA43.A551 1995   510.79′47453A551—dc20   94-073771
ISBN 0-9626401-6-6

The paper used in this book is acid-free. ∞

Library of Congress Catalog Card Number: 94-073771
ISBN 0-9626401-6-6

Printed in the United States of America.
10 9 8 7 6 5 4 3 2

2nd printing, April 2006

Dedication

To Harry Ruderman (1912–1994)

Harry Ruderman was a treasured member of the mathematics community who influenced and inspired generations of students and teachers. He himself was a remarkable teacher who promoted quality and substance in mathematics education. His name was well known to readers of professional journals and members of our organizations as a prolific writer, problemist, and lecturer. For over a decade, he served as a contributor and reviewer of ARML questions, and as chief judge of the competitions, thereby helping ensure the quality and success of these events. Most of all, Harry loved working with young people. He deepened their appreciation, strengthened their confidence, and instilled in them a sense of wonder and delight in doing mathematics.

Contents

Foreword

There are few celebrations of mathematics anywhere in the world that can compare with an ARML meet. This annual event brings together not only the best high school students of mathematics from most of the country, but also some of the most enthusiastic organizers of competitions. Many great teachers are among them. Others come from the ranks of former contestants who are presently coaching the younger generation, while still others are the "elders", who originally conceived and developed this wonderful competition. Unfortunately, fewer and fewer of the latter group are present, and we can pay tribute only to their memories.

My first ARML meet dates back to 1979, when at the invitation of Al Kalfus, I was privileged to present some awards to the winners. Subsequently, Al challenged me to bring a team from Texas. The idea greatly appealed to me; it was only much later that I discovered how much work it would take to gather the students, to make the necessary arrangements, and to finance the trip. Looking back, I can still hardly believe that I managed to pull it off in 1980, '81, and '82, and that Sam Baethge has managed to keep Texas in ARML ever since. I am certain that Sam, as well as the many other organizers of ARML teams, will agree with me: However much work it takes, there is nothing more satisfying than bringing a team of enthusiastic students to an ARML meet!

Prior to the meet itself, there is always a meeting of the coaches, organizers, and other interested parties. In the early years, they often lasted late into the night. In addition to providing a forum for discussing the details of the program and electing the officers of ARML, this meeting used to provide an opportunity for lively discussions about future plans. I still remember clearly the uproar caused by my suggestion (following a 24-hour bus ride from Texas) to move the meet more to the interior of the country; for a moment, I thought I would be lynched by the 80-100 other coaches! Fortunately, by the time I returned with the Indiana teams some years later, my outrageous idea was forgiven— and put into practice. With the addition of the Iowa site and the plans for having one in Las Vegas, we can be certain that ARML will truly become nationwide in the near-future. That was Al's dream, and we are all happy to see it come true.

It is often said that mathematics is not a spectator sport, but the ARML meets should be declared exceptions to that rule—at least, on occasions. There is nothing more spectacular than to observe nearly 1,000 students in a large gymnasium, intent on getting the correct answer to the next problem posed. The silence is truly deafening as they wait for the signal to start working; one can almost hear the racing of their thoughts as they busily formulate their answers. The variety of reactions following the announcement of the correct answers is most interesting. Everyone wants to know who got the correct answer and how the other members of his or her team are doing. The ongoing rivalry among the teams is most healthy. The partial scores posted several times during the meet make the competition even more exciting.

For most participants, an ARML meet represents not only an exciting day of superb competitions, but a wonderful opportunity for fellowship in mathematics. Many lasting friendships are formed among the students and coaches in attendance, and much excellent mathematics is done during the few hours of these meets. And many of the problems continue to challenge everyone for years to come.

While the spirit of the ARML meets can not be preserved in book form, the mathematical experiences of the last few ARML meets and the closely related NYSML contests are faithfully represented in this volume. These contests should provide many hours of pleasure and instruction, and inspire further investigations by all enthusiasts of this superb competition, as well as by others interested in creative problem solving.

In closing, I want to extend my sincere congratulations to Larry Zimmerman and Gil Kessler for the beautiful problems and solutions of this volume. Thanks also to Mark Saul and Steve Adrian for their excellent leadership in furthering and realizing

Al Kalfus's dreams, and to Stan Rabinowitz for adding yet one more masterpiece to the literature of mathematical competitions.

George Berzsenyi
Rose-Hulman Institute of Technology
Terre Haute, Indiana
October, 1994

Authors' Preface

Since its inception in 1976, ARML has grown from a regional competition involving about a dozen teams to a national event. It now draws over one hundred teams from the United States and Canada, and even entertained a visiting team from Russia. It has received support from the Mathematical Association of America, the National Council of Teachers of Mathematics, Mu Alpha Theta, and the National Council of Supervisors, as well as generous corporate support from Texas Instruments, Casio, and the Exxon Educational Foundation.

The highlight of the ARML weekend is the contest itself, eagerly anticipated by the students, teachers, and guests who gather for the world's largest on-site mathematics competition. ARML is currently run at two sites simultaneously, and will soon expand to others across the country.

As ARML expands, so does the opportunity for talented young people and dedicated teachers to come together to meet, compete, socialize, and receive the recognition they so justly deserve. New friendships are made, old friendships are renewed, traditions are established, and high spirits abound. The weekend also serves as a springboard for investigation and creative thinking that is inspired by the contest problems, by guest lecturers, and by the exchange of ideas.

This book contains the ARML contests from 1989 to 1994, the NYSML contests from 1989 to 1992, and the complete set of tie-breaker questions from 1983 to 1994. This group of contests is the last of the competitions that we authored since we became principal problems writers in 1983.

Many people have contributed to the quality and success of these contests, and we wish to express to them a debt of gratitude. Harry Ruderman was a friend and colleague who was always there to assist and inspire. He served as chief reviewer of the problems and contributed many original ideas that figured prominently in power questions. His sense of judgment and keen insights were always refreshing and revealing.

Since 1983, Professor Eugene Levine has also served as question reviewer. He too has offered valuable comments and suggestions. Our reviewing committee has also included Professors Niel Shell and Scott Hochwald, and we express out thanks to them. We wish to extend our appreciation to Bruce Beckett who, over a two year period, contributed some outstanding questions, including the basic premise for one of the NYSML power questions.

Special thanks go to Joe Wolfson, André Samson, and Barbara Rockow for supplying the information regarding team and individual winners. Thanks also to Mark Saul, president of ARML, to Steve Adrian, president of NYSML, and to the Executive Boards of both organizations for their wholehearted support.

Finally, we thank Stanley Rabinowitz, president of MathPro Press, for his enthusiasm, and for his helpful suggestions concerning the production of this book.

Larry Zimmerman
Gil Kessler
New York City
April 1994

Publisher's Preface

The ARML Competition is an impressive sight. I have been fortunate on several occasions to have been invited to help out at an ARML "meet" at Penn State University. To see almost 1,000 students competing and enjoying mathematics under one roof is inspiring and gratifying.

It is a tribute to the quality of the problems and the efficiency of the organizing committee that these students trek here from all over the country. Many get in buses early in the morning and ride the whole day for the privilege and excitement of participating in the ARML event, as well as meeting old and new friends.

The problems in this book cover the ARML contests from 1989 to 1994 and the NYSML contests from 1989 to 1992. These are the contests for which Larry Zimmerman and Gil Kessler were the principal authors and which have not appeared previously in book form. These authors are well-known for their interesting and original problems. When they present a talk at a mathematics conference, people flock to fill up the room to see their lively presentation. This excitement carries over to the problems that they create. There are dozens, perhaps hundreds of smaller city and state math leagues from all over the country; yet somehow the ARML and NYSML contests seem to stand out as unique and distinct. I am therefore pleased to be able to present these problems to you now.

We have changed very little in the statements of the problems. (They were correct and precise to begin with!) The notation was changed in a few places to be consistent with other books in this series and the solutions were somewhat expanded. See the glossary at the end of the book if you are uncertain about the terminology or notation used. In several instances, the authors had underlined important phrases in the problem statements that they did not want students to overlook under the pressure of the time constraints imposed. While helpful during the competition, such emphasis was deemed unnecessary when presenting the problems in book form. We have not modified the diagrams, but please note that the figures are not necessarily to scale.

We hope you will enjoy the variety and originality of these problems. The "power questions" are especially noteworthy. These are almost mini-research problems. They guide the students along and give them a feel for what mathematical research is like. They inevitably spawn additional research by students well after the contests are over. For example, in a year when the power question involved lattice points, you would find an unusually high number of Westinghouse projects later that year investigating properties of lattice points.

The "relay races" are also fun to watch at one of these meets. As soon as one student gets an answer to a problem, he or she passes the solution back to the next student in line. It is rare to find "power questions" or "relay races" in other math league competitions. We hope that these problems can be put to good use as practice problems for future competitions and to enliven the learning of mathematics in the classroom.

Stanley Rabinowitz
MathPro Press
Westford, Massachusetts
October, 1994

Introduction

The American Regions Mathematics League (ARML) competition is an annual national event that attracts a wide audience from across the United States and Canada. The New York State Mathematics League (NYSML) competition is also an annual event, drawing teams primarily from New York State. Both contests are identical in format, each offering four basic rounds for the 15-member teams. The students compete both jointly and individually.

The TEAM ROUND consists of 10 short answer questions whose difficulty level varies from easy to quite formidable. Team members distribute the problems among themselves, using whatever strategy they deem best suited for swift and accurate completion under the imposed time limit.

The POWER QUESTION is a challenging, multi-section problem usually focused about a single mathematical theme. It requires in-depth analysis and original thinking on the part of the entire team. Within a one-hour time limit, the students must produce a well written, mathematically accurate solution, including all necessary proofs. Over the years, we have received numerous letters indicating that power questions have served as the basis of classroom enrichment, student research papers, and Westinghouse Science Talent Search projects.

The contestants then gather in a large auditorium for the INDIVIDUAL ROUND. Here each participant works independently on a set of 8 short answer questions. These are administered in pairs, with ten minutes allowed for each pair. The results of this round are used to determine individual awards, while the scores also contribute to the team total.

For the RELAY ROUND, each team splits into groups of three. Within each sub-team, the first person solves his or her problem and passes the answer back. This number is needed for the solution of the second person's problem. The second person then passes an answer back. How quickly the third person produces the final answer determines the number of points awarded the team.

TIEBREAKERS are used to break ties among the individual top scores. While the entire audience tries these problems (flashed on overheads), those top scorers race the clock to submit the correct answer.

This book includes the ARML contests from 1989 to 1994, the NYSML contests from 1989 to 1992, and the tiebreakers back to 1983. An answer key is provided separate from the section containing complete solutions to all problems. These solutions have often been selected on the basis of instructional value rather than simply being the shortest approach. Frequently, extensions and directions for further investigation are suggested. The problems are indexed by topic. A listing of team and individual winners is also included.

The contests themselves represent only a beginning. What takes place after the competition is of great importance. The problems and solutions are a source of challenging material for contest practice, for classroom discussion, and for further mathematical research leading to student projects. They are also a great source of enjoyment.

For additional information about ARML, contact:

> Dr. Mark Saul
> 711 Amsterdam Avenue, Apt. 27K
> New York, NY 10025

For additional information about NYSML, contact:

> Mr. Steven Adrian
> 55 Mill Plain Road, Unit 29-5
> Danbury, CT 06811

ARML PROBLEMS

1989
American Regions
Mathematics League

Power Question—Pythagorean Polygons

A convex n-gon will be called "Pythagorean" if it has integer sides, it is cyclic, and its longest side is a diameter for its circumscribing circle. It shall be denoted by Pn or $Pn{:}(a, b, \ldots)$, where $a, b, \ldots$ are the lengths of its sides. WE SHALL ALWAYS USE THE LETTER d FOR ITS LONGEST SIDE. [Thus $P3$ is a Pythagorean triangle. Note that it would be a right triangle.]

I. [There is a theorem which states (in part) that: If a prime d is the hypotenuse of a Pythagorean triangle, then d^2 is the hypotenuse of two Pythagorean triangles, d^3 is the hypotenuse of three Pythagorean triangles, etc.]
    A. Find two $P3$'s for which $d = 25$.
    B. Find three $P3$'s for which $d = 125$.

II. Ptolemy's Theorem states: A convex quadrilateral is cyclic if and only if the product of its diagonals equals the sum of the products of the two pairs of opposite sides.

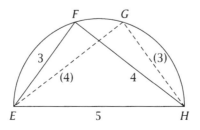

A. If the $P3{:}(3,4,5)$ is reflected as shown, a quadrilateral $EFGH$ can be formed (it will not be a $P4$, as FG is not an integer). Multiplying each side by 5 produces a $P4$. Find the sides of this $P4$.

B. Find a $P4$ with two equal sides and with $d = 25$ that is different from the answer to part IIA. [Note: Two Pn's are *not* considered different if their sides are equal, but in a different order.]

C. Show that a Pn must exist for all integers $n \geq 3$. [This may be done by describing how to create such a Pn.]

III. A. For the $P3{:}(a,b,d)$, $d^2 = a^2 + b^2$. Prove that for the $P4{:}(a,b,c,d)$, $d^2 > a^2 + b^2 + c^2$.

B. Given the $P4{:}(a,b,c,d)$, prove that if $d > 2$, then d must be composite.

C. If all the diagonals of a Pn are integers, we will call it "Super Pythagorean" and denote it by $\overline{P}n$.

1. Show that the area of any $\overline{P}4$ must be an integer. [*Hint*: One approach might be to first show that the area of any $\overline{P}4$ must be rational, and its perimeter must be even.]

2. *Assuming* that the area of every $\overline{P}3$ and every $\overline{P}4$ is an integer, show that (for all $n > 4$) the area of every $\overline{P}n$ must be an integer. [You may do this part even if part IIIC1 has not been completed.]

Team Questions

T1. The sum of the squares of three consecutive positive odd integers is a 4-digit number, all of whose digits are identical. Compute this 4-digit number.

T2. Compute the number of perfect cubes from 1 through 500,000 inclusive that are multiples of 7.

T3. If p and q are primes whose product is 1 less than a perfect square, and $p > 100$, compute the largest integer that must divide the sum $p + q$.

T4. In triangle ABC, angle bisectors $\overline{AD}$ and $\overline{BE}$ intersect at P. If $a = 3$, $b = 5$, $c = 7$, $BP = x$, and $PE = y$, compute the ratio $x : y$, where x and y are relatively prime integers.

T5. John throws a fair 6-sided die. If it comes up greater than 3, he wins. If not, he throws again and wins if it comes up greater than 4. If not, he throws again and wins only if it comes up greater than 5. Compute the probability that John wins.

T6. The accompanying diagram contains several sets of circles that "line up" (3 circles to a line). There are five such "lines". The integers from 1 through 7 are to be inserted, one number to a circle, so that the sum of the three numbers in each line is the same (this can be done in many ways). Which number can *not* be placed in the lower left circle?

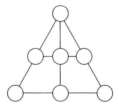

T7. [Note: A tangent line to the curve $y = x^2$ at the point (a, a^2) will have slope $2a$.]

The angle formed by the tangents to $y = x^2$ from the point (r, s) in Quadrant II is bisected by the line through (r, s) with slope 1. Compute s.

T8. Compute the length of the tangent segment from the origin to the circle that passes through the points $(3, 4)$, $(6, 8)$, and $(5, 13)$.

T9. [Note: The notation "draw $\overset{\frown}{XY}$" means draw a circular arc with point X as center and length XY as radius.]

The arc shown is a semicircle. Point O is the midpoint of $\overline{ABC}$, $AB = 8$, and $BC = 6$. We perform the following constructions with compasses and straightedge:

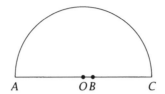

$\left\{\begin{array}{l} \text{1.} \quad \text{Draw } \underset{\frown}{BC}, \text{ crossing } \overline{AO} \text{ at } D. \\ \text{2.} \quad \text{Draw } \underset{\frown}{DC} \text{ and } \underset{\frown}{CD}, \text{ crossing at } E. \\ \text{3.} \quad \text{Draw } \overleftrightarrow{BE}, \text{ crossing the semicircle at } F. \end{array}\right.$

4. Draw $\underset{\frown}{AO}$, crossing the semicircle at G.

If $FG = \sqrt{k}$, compute the integer k.

T10. Two circles are externally tangent at point P, as shown. Segment $\overline{CPD}$ is parallel to common external tangent $\overline{AB}$. If the radii of the circles are 2 and 18, compute the distance between the midpoints of $\overline{AB}$ and $\overline{CD}$.

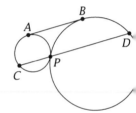

Individual Questions

I1. If x is a positive integer and $x(x + 1)(x + 2)(x + 3)+1 = 379^2$, compute x.

I2. The bisectors of the angles of quadrilateral $ABCD$ are drawn. They form quadrilateral $EFGH$, as shown, in which $\angle E + \angle F = 193°$. If $\angle A > \angle C$, compute the numerical value of $\angle A - \angle C$.

[For clarification, $\angle E$ means $\angle HEF$, $\angle F$ means $\angle EFG$, $\angle A$ means $\angle DAB$, and $\angle C$ means $\angle BCD$.]

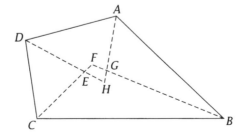

I3. If $P(x)$ is a polynomial in x, and $x^{23} + 23x^{17} - 18x^{16} - 24x^{15} + 108x^{14} = (x^4 - 3x^2 - 2x + 9) \cdot P(x)$ for all values of x, compute the sum of the coefficients of $P(x)$.

I4. If the area of a rectangle is $1/2$ of the area of its circumscribed circle, compute the acute angle between the diagonals of the rectangle to the nearest degree. [We will accept any integer answer that is no more than $4°$ away from the correct answer to this problem.] [Reminder: Calculators may *not* be used!]

I5. If the terms in the successive rows of Pascal's Triangle (as shown here) are written successively, we form the sequence $1, 1, 1, 1, 2,$ $1, 1, 3, 3, 1, 1, 4, 6, 4, 1, 1, 5, 10, 10, \ldots$. If the sum of the first 212 terms of this sequence is $2^k + k$, compute the integer k.

$$
\begin{array}{ccccccccc}
 & & & & 1 & & & & \\
 & & & 1 & & 1 & & & \\
 & & 1 & & 2 & & 1 & & \\
 & 1 & & 3 & & 3 & & 1 & \\
1 & & 4 & & 6 & & 4 & & 1 \\
 & & & & \text{etc.} & & & &
\end{array}
$$

I6. (Note: In this problem, the brackets represent the Greatest Integer Function.) Compute the smallest positive integer x greater than 9 such that

$$[x] - 19 \cdot \left[\frac{x}{19}\right] = 9 = [x] - 89 \cdot \left[\frac{x}{89}\right].$$

I7. In order to list the integers from 0 through 7 in binary notation $[0, 1, 10, 11, 100, 101, 110, 111]$, we must write twelve 1's. Compute the number of 1's needed to list, in binary notation, the integers from 0 through 1023.

I8. A convex hexagon is inscribed in a circle. If its successive sides are 2, 2, 7, 7, 11, and 11, compute the diameter of the circumscribed circle.

Relay #1

R1-1. Let n be the number you will pass back. Pass back the numerical value of $6\sqrt{n} - 9$.

R1-2. Let T = TNYWR, and let $k = T - 4$.

Compute the volume of a cube whose main diagonal (the one through the center of the cube) is $k\sqrt{3}$.

R1-3. Let T = TNYWR, and let $k = \frac{T}{25} - 3$.

For positive integers a, b, and c, we define $a \equiv b$ (MAD c) if and only if c is a divisor of $(a + b)$. Compute the smallest positive integer $x > 1$ such that $kx^3 + 5 \equiv 17$ (MAD 3).

Relay #2

R2-1. The year 1989 = $9 \cdot 13 \cdot 17$. Compute the next greater year that can be written as the product of three positive integers in arithmetic progression, given that the sum of those integers is 57.

R2-2. Let T = TNYWR, and let $n = \frac{T+5}{1000}$.

Compute the positive number x such that $x^{\log_{19} 89} = 89^n$.

R2-3. Let k = TNYWR.

A set of n tangent congruent semicircles are formed to exactly fit along the diameter of the large semicircle as shown. If the shaded area (that is, the area inside the large semicircle but outside the small semicircles) is k times the total area of the small semicircles, compute n.

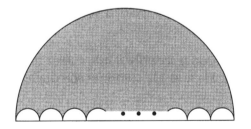

1990
American Regions
Mathematics League

Power Question—Diophantine Equations

In the following equations, *all* letters represent positive integers, and $a > b$.

Let us examine the expression $a^3 + b^3$, where $a > b$. One well-known result is that $a^3 + b^3 = c^3$ has no solution in positive integers. For each of the equations in parts I and II, either:

1. Prove that no solutions can exist   OR
2. Show how an infinite number of solutions can be generated.

I. A. $a^3 + b^3 = c^2$

    B. $a^3 + b^3 = c \cdot d \cdot e$,

                where c, d, and e are in geometric progression

    C. $a^3 + b^3 = c \cdot d \cdot e$,

                where c, d, and e are in arithmetic progression

    D. $a^3 + b^3 = 3p$, where p is a prime greater than 3

II. A. $a^3 + b^3 = 2^c$

     B. $a^3 + b^3 = 3^c$

     C. $a^3 + b^3 = p^c$, where p is a prime greater than 3

III. Assuming that $a^3 + b^3 = c!$ has solutions, and c is at least 12:

     A. Prove that the largest prime less than c does not divide a.

     B. Prove that $a + b$ is a multiple of 330.

Team Questions

T1.   In the addition problem at the right, each letter   AB
represents a different digit. Compute the difference   CD
between the greatest possible value for this sum and   EF
the greatest possible *odd* value for this sum.   GH
                                                     +   IJ

T2.   Three vertices of a cube in space have coordinates $A(2,3,0)$, $B(0,5,4)$, and $C(4,1,8)$. Compute the coordinates of the center of the cube.

T3.   When expanded as a decimal, the fraction 1/97 has a repetend (the repeating part of the decimal) that begins right after the decimal point and is 96 digits long. If the last three digits of the repetend are A67, compute the digit A.

T4.   A soldier is last in a 1/8 mile long line of troops that is marching forward at a steady 2 mph. At a given moment, he begins to run toward the front of the line; when he reaches the first person, he immediately runs back to the end of the line (which has, of course, changed location). If he runs at a steady 4 mph, losing no time in reversing direction, compute the total distance he has run (in miles).

T5.   An open-top rectangular box can be formed by cutting identical squares off the four corners of a rectangular piece of cardboard, and folding up the four sections that then stick out. For a particular sized piece of cardboard, the same volume results whether squares of side 1 or squares of side 2 have been cut out. Compute the resulting volume if squares of side 3 are cut out.

T6.   Compute the number of integers between 100,000 and one million with the property that their digits are distinct and increase from left to right.

T7.   Compute all integer values of n, $90 \le n \le 100$, that can *not* be written in the form $n = a + b + ab$, where a and b are positive integers.

T8. In quadrilateral $ABCD$, $AB = 2\sqrt{6}, BC = 7 - 2\sqrt{3}, CD = 5$, $\angle B = 135°$, and $\angle C = 120°$. Compute AD.

T9. A strictly increasing sequence of *positive* integers contains the terms 305 and 1990. If each term after the second is equal to the sum of the two previous terms, compute the least possible value for the first term.

T10. If
$$\tan(120° - x) = \frac{\sin 120° - \sin x}{\cos 120° - \cos x},$$
where $0° < x < 180°$, compute x.

Individual Questions

I1. Compute
$$\frac{(1990)^3 - (1000)^3 - (990)^3}{(1990)(1000)(990)}.$$

I2. The formula $F = \frac{9}{5}C + 32$ converts Celcius (C) temperature into Farenheit (F). A student who forgot the correct formula used the equation $F = 2C + 30$ instead. This equation actually produces values of F that are no more than $1°$ away from the correct values (yielded by the formula) if and only if $a° \le C \le b°$. Compute the ordered pair (a, b).

I3. If $a + b = c$, $b + c = d$, $c + d = a$, and b is a positive integer, compute the greatest possible value for $a + b + c + d$.

I4. The letters A, B, and C represent different digits, A is a prime, and A − B = 4. If the number AAABBBC is a prime, compute the ordered triple (A, B, C).

I5. Compute the integer $k, k > 2$, for which
$$\log(k - 2)! + \log(k - 1)! + 2 = 2\log k!.$$

I6. Compute the smallest positive value of x, *in degrees*, for which the function $f(x) = \sin\frac{x}{3} + \sin\frac{x}{11}$ achieves its maximum value.

I7.   Find the largest value of x for which $x^2 + y^2 = x + y$ has a solution, if x and y are real.

I8.   The smallest (in area) triangle with integer area and consecutive integer sides has sides 3,4,5. The next larger such triangle has sides 13,14,15. Compute the three sides of the next larger such triangle, given that its "middle" side is a multiple of 4.

Relay #1

R1-1. Two sides of an isosceles triangle are 22 and 61. Compute the area of the triangle.

R1-2. Let T = TNYWR, and let $K = T + 1$.

If a, b, and c are positive integers, each less than or equal to K, and if $P * Q$ means $\frac{P+Q}{2}$, compute the greatest possible value for the expression $a * (b * c) - (a * b) * c$.

R1-3. Let T = TNYWR.

(Note: In this problem, the brackets represent the Greatest Integer Function.)   Compute the number of values of n, with $1 < n < T$, for which $[\frac{n}{2}] + [\frac{n}{3}] = \frac{n}{2} + \frac{n}{3}$.

Relay #2

R2-1. Each side of a rectangular box is an integer greater than 1. The sum of the areas of two adjacent faces is 25. Compute the area of the face that is adjacent to these two.

R2-2. Let T = TNYWR, and let $K = 12T - 5$.

[Note: When a large integer such as 12,345,678,901 is written, the "usual way" to place commas is to put a comma after every third digit, counting from right to left (as shown).]

The number 31416 followed by K zeros is written down, with commas placed in the "usual way". Compute the number of commas needed.

R2-3. Let k = TNYWR.

In the diagram, triangle ABC is equilateral with side equal to 20; $\overline{PQ}\|\overline{BC}, \overline{QR}\|\overline{AB}$, and $\overline{RS}\|\overline{CA}$. If $PQ + QR + RS = k$, compute PS.

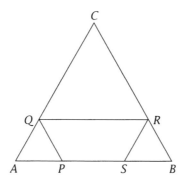

1991
American Regions
Mathematics League

Power Question—"Nice" Angles and Polygons

DEFINITION 1:   We call angle A "nice" if *both* sin A and cos A are rational.

DEFINITION 2:   We call a convex polygon "nice" if all of its interior angles are "nice".

I.   Prove each of the following:

   1a.   If angle A is nice, its supplement will be nice.

   1b.   If angle A is nice, $\frac{1}{2}A$ need not be nice, but $2A$ will be nice.

   1c.   The set of nice angles is closed under addition.

   2a.   [Note: A Pythagorean triangle is a right triangle with integer sides.] Every acute nice angle is the angle of some Pythagorean triangle.

   2b.   If angle A is an acute nice angle and cos $A = b/c$, where b and c are relatively prime positive integers, then c will be odd.

   2c.   There is no smallest positive nice angle.

II.   1.   Prove that if the sides of a triangle are rational, and one angle is nice, then the other angles will be nice. [Be sure you satisfy both parts of Definition 1.]

2a.   Find the sides of an *acute* nice triangle whose sides are integers and whose perimeter is less than 20. [Be sure that this triangle is both acute and nice.]

2b.   Prove that if the sides of a nice triangle are integers, its area will be an *even integer*. [Hint: One approach would be to first show that its perimeter must be even.]

III.   A convex quadrilateral has the following properties:

1.   Its sides are integers whose product is a square.

2.   It can be inscribed in a circle, and can be circumscribed about (another) circle.

Prove that this quadrilateral is nice.

Team Questions

T1.   You have 121 marbles, some of which are red, some white, and the rest blue. You also have 10 jars. If all the marbles are distributed into the jars, there *must* be a jar with at least n marbles of the same color. Compute the maximum possible value for n.

T2.   [Note: A palindrome is a positive integer that reads backwards the same as it reads forwards. For example: 67276.]

The sum of two 4-digit palindromes is the 5-digit palindrome N. Compute the maximum possible value for N.

T3.   Compute the smallest positive integer $n > 100$ such that $\binom{n}{101}$ is divisible by $\binom{n}{100}$, but is not equal to it.

T4.   If $(x^2 + x + 1)(x^6 + x^3 + 1) = \frac{10}{x-1}$, compute the real value of x.

T5.   Compute the number of real values of x that satisfy the equation $\big| |x^2 - 1| - 1 \big| = 2^x$. [Note: The vertical bars are absolute value signs.]

T6.   One angle of a triangle is twice another, and the sides opposite these angles have lengths 15 and 9. Compute the length of the third side of the triangle.

T7.   In the semicircle shown, diameter $P_0P_1 = 2$. Angle $P_0P_1P_2 = 1°$; angle $P_1P_2P_3 = 2°$; angle $P_2P_3P_4 = 3°;\ldots$; angle $P_{k-1}P_kP_{k+1} = k°$. If $\overline{P_kP_{k+1}}$ is the first chord whose length is less than 1, compute k.

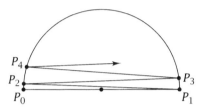

T8.   Let $x_n + iy_n = (1 + i\sqrt{3})^n$, where x_n and y_n are real and n is a positive integer. If $x_{19}y_{91} + x_{91}y_{19} = 2^k\sqrt{3}$, compute k.

T9.   The bases of an isosceles trapezoid are 18 and 30, and its altitude is 8. Using each leg of the trapezoid as a diameter, semicircles are drawn exterior to the trapezoid. If the midpoints of those arcs are P and Q, compute PQ.

T10. Compute the smallest positive integer that can *not* be the difference between a square and a prime, if the square is greater than the prime.

Individual Questions

I1.   Consider the system of 25 equations in 26 variables:

$$
\begin{aligned}
A + B &= 1 \\
B + C &= 2 \\
C + D &= 3 \\
&\cdots \\
X + Y &= 24 \\
Y + Z &= 25
\end{aligned}
$$

Compute $A + Z$.

I2.   Let $(1 - \frac{1}{3^2})(1 - \frac{1}{4^2})(1 - \frac{1}{5^2}) \cdots (1 - \frac{1}{1991^2}) = \frac{x}{1991}$. Compute the integer x.

I3.   The area of right triangle ABC is 4, and hypotenuse $\overline{AB}$ is 12. Compute $\sin 2A$.

I4.   Compute the x-coordinates of *each* of the five points on the line $y = 6$ that form an isosceles triangle with the points $(-5, 0)$ and $(5, 0)$.

I5.   (Note: In this problem, the brackets represent the Greatest Integer Function.)

Compute $\left[\dfrac{3^{31} + 2^{31}}{3^{29} + 2^{29}} \right]$.

I6.   Compute the area of the region that lies above the graph of $y = |x - 1| + |x - 3|$ but below the graph of $y = 8$.

I7.   Right triangle ABC (hypotenuse $\overline{AB}$) is inscribed in equilateral triangle PQR, as shown. If $PC = 3$, and $BP = CQ = 2$, compute AQ.

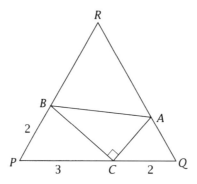

I8.   The number $85^9 - 21^9 + 6^9$ is divisible by an integer between 2,000 and 3,000. Compute that integer.

Relay #1

R1-1. Compute the smallest positive 3-digit multiple of 7 for which the sum of its digits is also a multiple of 7.

R1-2. Let T = TNYWR and let $B = T - 130$.

Compute $(B^{\log 4})(B^{\log 25})$.

R1-3. Let T = TNYWR.

Compute the smallest possible hypotenuse for a right triangle whose area is T.

Relay #2

R2-1. The roots of $ax^2 + bx + c = 0$ are 6 and p. The roots of $cx^2 + bx + a = 0$ are q and r. Compute the product pqr.

R2-2. Let T = TNYWR and let $L = 36T$.

$\overline{AEB}$ and $\overline{CDE}$ are common tangents to the two circles, as shown. If $AB = L$, and $AE = 2(EB)$, compute CD.

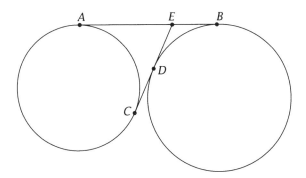

R2-3. Let Q = TNYWR. [Reminder: "Lattice points" are points on a grid, both of whose coordinates are integers.]

The circle $(x-1)^2 + (y-2)^2 = 31$ does not go through any lattice points. Compute the coordinates of lattice point P, in quadrant Q, that is outside this circle but is closest to it.

1992
American Regions
Mathematics League

Power Question—Lattice Points on a Parabola

Throughout this problem, the points $A(a, a^2), B(b, b^2), C(c, c^2)$, and $D(d, d^2)$ represent distinct lattice points on the parabola $y = x^2$.

I.   Let the area of triangle ABC be K. It can be shown that

$$K = \frac{1}{2} |(a - b)(b - c)(c - a)|.$$

   1.   Show that K must be an integer.
   2.   Show that $K = 3$ is the only possible prime value for K.
   3.   Show that K cannot be the square of a prime.
   4.   Show that the area of quadrilateral $ABCD$ cannot be 8.

II.   It can be shown that the slope of $\overleftrightarrow{AB}$ is $a + b$.
   1.   A line passes through the point (3,5) and through two lattice points on $y = x^2$. Compute the coordinates of these two points. Be sure to find all possible pairs of such points.
   2.   A line passes through the point (2,4) and through three other lattice points on the "double parabola" $y^2 = x^4$. Compute the coordinates of these three points. Be sure to find all possible triplets of such points.

III.   Consider the quadrilateral $ABCD$. [Remember that the slope of $\overleftrightarrow{AB}$, for example, is $a + b$.]

1. Let the vertices be labeled (alphabetically) in a counter-clockwise direction. Show that

$$\tan A = \frac{d - b}{1 + (a + b)(a + d)}.$$

2. A quadrilateral is "cyclic" if all four of its vertices lie on the same circle.

   Show that: If quadrilateral $ABCD$ is cyclic, then $a + b + c + d = 0$; AND

   If $a + b + c + d = 0$, then quadrilateral $ABCD$ is cyclic.

3. Use the previous result to show that:

   If a circle intersects the graph of $y = x^2$ in four points, and three of them are lattice points, then the fourth must also be a lattice point.

Team Questions

T1.   Consider the set of 5-digit numbers, each of which is a permutation of the digits 1,2,3,4,5. There are 120 numbers in this set. Compute the sum of these numbers.

T2.   The circles whose equations are $x^2 + y^2 - 4x + 2y - 11 = 0$ and $x^2 + y^2 - 14x + 12y + 60 = 0$ intersect in the points A and B. Compute the slope of $\overleftrightarrow{AB}$.

T3.   The shorter base of an *integer-sided* isosceles trapezoid is 3. Altitudes are drawn from the ends of this base, and they cut the trapezoid into three equal areas. Compute the minimum possible perimeter for the trapezoid.

T4.   Compute the positive integer value of k that makes the following statement true:

For all positive integers a, b, and c that make the roots of $ax^2 + bx + c = 0$ rational, the roots of $4ax^2 + 12bx + kc = 0$ will also be rational.

T5. (In this problem, the brackets represent the Greatest Integer Function.)

If $\sin x° + \cos x° = \tan x°, 0 < x < 135$, compute $[\frac{x}{10}]$.

T6. Points P, Q, and R are the midpoints of the medians of triangle ABC. If the area of triangle ABC is 1,024, compute the area of triangle PQR.

T7. Compute $\sqrt{(111,111,111,111)(1,000,000,000,005)+1}$.

T8. Let z and $z + 1$ be complex nth roots of 1. If n is a positive integer multiple of 5, compute the smallest possible value for $n + z^3$.

T9. Segment $\overline{AB}$ is the diameter of the semicircle shown; O is the midpoint of $\overline{AB}$. Circle P is tangent to $\overline{AB}$ at O and to the semi-circle; circle Q is tangent to $\overline{AB}$, to the semicircle, and to circle P as shown. If $OB = 1$, compute the radius of circle Q.

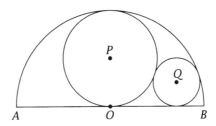

T10. In a 3-dimensional coordinate system with x-, y-, and z-axes, P is a point on the line $y = -x + 1$ in the xy-plane and Q is a point on the line $z = -2x + 1$ in the xz-plane. Compute the smallest possible value for PQ.

Individual Questions

I1. The product of my age 21 years ago and my age 21 years from now is the cube of a prime. Compute my age now.

I2.   The successive sides of a quadrilateral are 2, 6, 9, and x. If the diagonals of the quadrilateral are perpendicular, compute x.

I3.   If the 3-digit positive integer n = ABC = AB + BA + AC + CA + BC + CB, compute the largest possible value for n.

I4.   Consider the sequence 1, 2, 2, 3, 3, 3, 4, 4, 4, 4, ... , where the integer n appears n times. Compute the 1992nd term of this sequence.

I5.   If L_n represents the number of lattice points on the graph of $|x| + |y| = n$, for positive integer n, compute the value of

$$L_1 - L_2 + L_3 - L_4 + L_5 - L_6 + \cdots + L_{999} - L_{1000}.$$

I6.   The sides of an isosceles triangle are $\cos x, \cos x$, and $\cos 7x$, and its vertex angle is $2x$. [All angle measurements are in degrees.] Compute *all three* possible values of x.

I7.   (Note: In this problem, the brackets represent the Greatest Integer Function.) Compute the number of intersection points of the graphs of

$$(x - [x])^2 + y^2 = x - [x] \quad \text{and}$$

$$y = \tfrac{1}{5}x.$$

I8.   In triangle ABC, points D and E are on $\overline{AB}$ and $\overline{AC}$, and angle-bisector $\overline{AT}$ intersects $\overline{DE}$ at F [as shown in the diagram]. If $AD = 1, DB = 3, AE = 2$, and $EC = 4$, compute the ratio $AF : AT$.

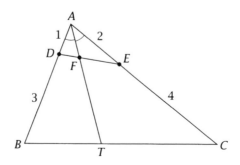

RELAY #1

R1-1. The product of five consecutive positive integers is divisible by both 13 and 31. If that product is as small as possible, compute the smallest of the five integers.

R1-2. Let T = TNYWR and let $K = \frac{T-1}{15}$.

Compute the value of $(1 - i)^{2K}$.

R1-3. Let T = TNYWR.

Three vertices of a cube are connected to form a triangle. Compute the maximum possible perimeter for this triangle if the edge of the cube is T.

Relay #2

R2-1. Compute the largest integer less than 125 that has a prime number of distinct (positive) factors.

R2-2. Let T = TNYWR and let $K = T/11$.

If $\log_n 2 = K$, and $n > 1$, compute $\log_4 n$.

R2-3. Let T = TNYWR and let $r = 1/T$.

For integer $n \geq 0$, $F(n + 1) = x \cdot F(n) + 1$, and $F(0) = 1$.

Express $(x - 1) \cdot F(r)$ as a polynomial in x with integer coefficients.

[Note: The answer is *not* to be expressed in factored form, and is to be simplified as much as possible!]

1993
American Region
Mathematics League

Power Question—Calculations and Approximations

The use of calculators is permitted for this question.

I. APPROXIMATIONS

    A. Each of the following relations defines a sequence of numbers $x_1, x_2, x_3, \ldots$. In each case, *calculate* x_2 and x_{12} to six decimal places (do not round off), and *conjecture* what the limiting value of the sequence is as n increases without bound:

        1. $x_{n+1} = \frac{1}{2}\left(x_n + \frac{64}{x_n}\right)$, $x_1 = 100$;

        2. $x_{n+1} = \frac{1}{3}\left(2x_n + \frac{64}{x_n^2}\right)$, $x_1 = 100$;

        3. $x_{n+1} = \sqrt{\sqrt{64x_n}}$, $x_1 = 100$.

    B. Based on examples A1 and A2 above, *create* a similar relation whose limiting value is the 5th root of 64. Justify your answer.

II. ARCHIMEDES

    In circle O, of radius 1, we construct a sequence of chords $\overline{PA_0}, \overline{PA_1}, \overline{PA_2}, \ldots, \overline{PA_n}, \ldots$, all with common endpoint P. Furthermore, for all n, arc $\overparen{PA_{n+1}} = \frac{1}{2}(\text{arc } \overparen{PA_n})$. The diagram shows two such chords, $\overline{PA_n}$ and $\overline{PA_{n+1}}$. Let the length of chord $\overline{PA_i} = 2x_i$, and the distance from center O to the chord be d_i.

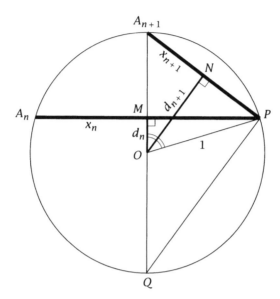

A. Let angle $POA_{n+1} = \theta$. Using the formula for $\cos \frac{1}{2}\theta$, show
    that $d_{n+1} = \sqrt{\frac{1+d_n}{2}}$.

B. By comparing the areas of triangles OPA_{n+1} and QPA_{n+1},
    show that $x_{n+1} = \frac{x_n}{2d_{n+1}}$.

C. Let $S_n = 2^{n+1}x_n$ for $n = 0, 1, 2, \ldots$. Show that $S_{n+1} = \frac{S_n}{d_{n+1}}$.

D. Let $d_0 = 0$ and $S_0 = 2x_0 = 2$. Using IIA and IIC above,
    calculate S_1 and S_7 to six decimal places. *Conjecture* what
    the limiting value of S_n is as n increases without bound,
    and briefly justify your conjecture.

III. "SUM" ADDITIONAL PROBLEMS

Let $L_n = r^n + s^n$ for all positive integers n, where $r = \frac{1+\sqrt{5}}{2}$ and
$s = \frac{1-\sqrt{5}}{2}$.

A. Calculate $L_1, L_2, L_3, L_4, L_5, L_6, L_7$, and L_8.

B. Show that $L_{n+1} = L_n + L_{n-1}$. [You may wish to use the
    identity $r^{n+1} + s^{n+1} = (r^n + s^n)(r + s) - r^n s - r s^n$.]

C. *Calculate* $r, r^2, r^3, r^4, r^5, r^6, r^7$, and r^8 (two decimal places
    will be sufficient). *Conjecture* how you can obtain L_n by only
    using r^n.

D. Compute the number of digits in L_{201}.

E. Compute the smallest integer n for which L_n has 21 digits.
    Also compute the smallest integer n for which L_n has 200
    digits.

F. The Fibonacci numbers can be obtained from the formula $F_n = \frac{1}{\sqrt{5}}(r^n - s^n)$, for all positive integers n. Compute the smallest integer n for which F_n has 21 digits, and write the first four digits of that F_n.

Team Questions

T1. In the addition below, different letters represent different digits. Compute the 5-digit number YUCCA.

$$\begin{array}{r} \text{LARRY} \\ + \text{ GIL} \\ \hline \text{YUCCA} \end{array}$$

T2. The sides of a rectangle are 1 and 3, and its diagonals intersect forming an angle of $\theta°$. Compute $\sin \theta°$.

T3. Compute x if $\text{Arctan } x + \text{Arctan } 1 = 2(\text{Arctan } x - \text{Arctan } \frac{1}{3})$.

T4. The number of different 10-letter "words" that can be made from the letters of the word REASSESSES is the same as the number of different x-letter "words" that can be made from the letters of the word REDUCTIONS. Compute x. [Note: The term "word" refers to any arrangement of letters.]

T5. Circles P and Q are tangent, and each has radius 1. Segment $\overline{PQ}$ extended meets the circles at A and B, and $\overline{AC}$ and $\overline{BTC}$ are tangents to circle P, as shown in the diagram. Compute AC.

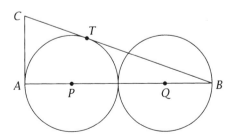

T6. The number $(7^{12} + 4^{12})$ is the product of three 4-digit primes, exactly one of which is greater than 2,626. Compute this largest prime factor.

T7. The probability that 11 consecutive throws of a pair of ordinary fair dice will each have a different total can be written in the form $\frac{(a!)(b!)(c!)}{36^d}$ where a, b, c, and d are integers and $a \le b \le c \le d$. Compute the ordered quadruple (a, b, c, d).

T8. The arithmetic mean of the positive numbers $a_1, a_2, \ldots, a_k$ is one-fourth of the arithmetic mean of the positive numbers $b_1, b_2, \ldots, b_{7k}$ (where k is a positive integer). *If both of these means are integers*, compute the smallest possible integer value for the arithmetic mean of $a_1, a_2, \ldots, a_k, b_1, b_2, \ldots, b_{7k}$.

T9. Two right circular cones have parallel bases (that is, their bases lie in parallel planes), and the apex of each is (at) the center of the base of the other. The cones intersect in circle C. If the areas of the bases are 400 and 900, compute the area of circle C.

T10. [*Reminder*: The Fibonacci sequence is defined as follows: $F_1 = F_2 = 1$, and $F_n = F_{n-1} + F_{n-2}$ for $n \ge 3$.]

The Fibonacci numbers F_a, F_b, and F_c form an increasing arithmetic sequence. If $a + b + c = 2000$, compute a.

Individual Questions

I1. How many ordered pairs of positive integers (x, y), where $1993 < x < y < 2020$, satisfy the equation $y^2 - x^2 = 2x + 1$?

I2. Square $ABCD$ is positioned on the axes as shown. Compute the area of the square.

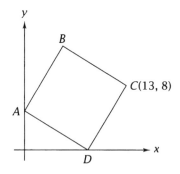

I3.   There is only one value of x for which the median and the arithmetic mean of the five numbers 4, 2, 16, 6, and x are equal. Compute that value of x.

I4.   Two of the diagonals of a convex equilateral pentagon are perpendicular. If one of the interior angles of the pentagon is $100°$, compute the measures of the *other four* interior angles.

I5.   Rearrange the following four quantities so that they are in *increasing* order of size (from left to right):

$$\sin 9°, \cos 67°, \sin 16° \cos 7°, \cos 16° \sin 7°.$$

[Reminder: calculators may *not* be used.]

I6.   If the tens digit of $(4A1)^{1A4}$ is 2, compute all possible values for the digit A. (Note: 4A1 and 1A4 represent 3-digit numbers.)

I7.   Compute the *number of real values of x* such that:

$$x^{100} - 4^x \cdot x^{98} - x^2 + 4^x = 0.$$

I8.   There are several values for a prime, p, with the property that any 5-digit multiple of p remains a multiple of p under "cyclic permutation". One such value is 41 (for example, since 50635 is a multiple of 41, so are 55063, 35506, 63550, and [0]6355); another such value of p is 3. Compute the value of p that is greater than 41.

Relay #1

R1-1. Let the 3-digit number $n = $ ABC. Compute the greatest possible value for $\frac{n}{A + B + C}$.

R1-2. Let $T = $ TNYWR.

Compute the units digit of $9^T \cdot 13^{T+1} \cdot 17^{T+2}$.

R1-3. Let $T = $ TNYWR.

Six non-overlapping circles, each of radius r, are internally tangent to a circle of radius $3T$. Compute the largest possible value for r.

Relay #2

R2-1. If a and b are positive integers with $a \neq b$, and $\frac{\log a}{\log b} = \frac{a}{b}$, compute the quantity $ab + 1$.

R2-2. Let $T = $ TNYWR.

Triangle AOB is positioned in the coordinate plane as shown. The slope of $\overline{OA}$ is 1; the slope of $\overline{OB}$ is 8; the slope of $\overline{AB}$ is T. Compute b/a.

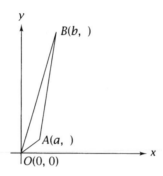

R2-3. Let $T = $ TNYWR.

If $a^2 + Tb^2 = 6ab$, compute the *larger* value of a/b.

1994
American Regions
Mathematics League

Power Question—Lattice Points

This question refers to figures in a 2-dimensional rectangular coordinate system only.

Lattice points are points on a grid, both of whose coordinates are integers. A *lattice segment* is a line segment whose endpoints are lattice points; an *oblique* lattice segment is one that is not parallel to either axis.

The letter l will represent the length of a lattice segment, as well as the segment itself. Let $N(l)$ represent the number of lattice points on a lattice segment of length l, NOT INCLUDING ITS ENDPOINTS. [For example, $N(\sqrt{2}) = 0$; $N(17) = 0$ if the segment is oblique, and $N(17) = 16$ if the segment is not oblique.]

1. Compute $N(l)$ for the lattice segment l whose endpoints are

    (a) $(0,0)$ and $(3,4)$;

    (b) $(0,0)$ and $(12,16)$;

    (c) $(0,0)$ and $(300,400)$;

    (d) $(-3,11)$ and $(57,101)$.

2. Compute all possible values for $N(l)$ if l is *oblique* and

    (a) $l = 13$;

    (b) $l = 4 \cdot 13$;

    (c) $l = 5 \cdot 13$ [be sure to consider *all* possible oblique positions for l].

3.   Compute the number of different possible values for $N(l)$ if l is oblique and $l = 5 \cdot 13 \cdot 17$.

A *lattice polygon* is a polygon whose vertices are lattice points; an *oblique* lattice polygon is one whose sides are all oblique.

Pick's Theorem: The area of any lattice polygon is given by $K = \frac{1}{2}B + I - 1$ [where K is the area, B is the number of lattice points on the boundary (sides and vertices) of the polygon, and I is the number of lattice points in the interior of the polygon].

4.   Compute the value of I (the number of interior lattice points) for the triangle whose vertices are $(1, 2)$, $(31, 42)$, and $(81, -78)$. SHOW ALL WORK.

5.   (a)   Compute the maximum value of I for a lattice square whose side is 25.

      (b)   Compute the maximum value of I for a lattice square whose side is 26.

6.   Show that if two sides of an *oblique* lattice triangle are 5 and 13, then the third side cannot be an integer.

7.   (a)   Given any five lattice points, show that there is a segment joining two of them that contains a lattice point (other than the endpoints of the segment).

      (b)   Prove that every convex lattice pentagon must contain an interior lattice point.

      (c)   A "trapezium" is a quadrilateral with *no* pair of parallel sides. For a convex lattice trapezium:

             (1)   Show that if two successive sides each contain a lattice point (other than the vertices), then there is a lattice point in the interior of the trapezium.

             (2)   Show that if there are two opposite sides neither of which contains a lattice point (other than the vertices), then there is a lattice point in the interior of the trapezium.

             [Together, these show that every convex lattice trapezium must contain an interior lattice point.]

8.   If the product of two sides of a lattice triangle is a prime, and the area is also a prime, prove that the area must be 2.

Team Questions

T1.   If
$$x^5 + 5x^4 + 10x^3 + 10x^2 - 5x + 1 = 10,$$

and $x \neq -1$, compute the numerical value of $(x + 1)^4$.

T2.   Two externally tangent circles have radii r and R, with $r < R$. Their common external tangent segments are extended until they meet at point P. If angle P is $60°$, compute the ratio $r : R$.

T3.   Consider the equation
$$100 \cdots 00_b + 100 \cdots 00_{b+1} = 100 \cdots 00_{b+2},$$

where each term contains exactly n zeros [note that each subscript indicates the base in which that term is written]. For how many values of n, $2 \leq n \leq 100$, will a solution [that is, a positive integer value of b] exist for the equation?

T4.   "An isosceles triangle has a median equal to 15 and an altitude equal to 24."

This information determines exactly two triangles. Compute the area of either one of these triangles. [Only give *one* answer.]

T5.   As t takes on all real values, the set of points (x, y) defined by
$$x = t^2 - 2, \quad y = t^3 - 9t + 5$$

forms a curve that crosses itself. Compute the ordered pair (x, y) where this crossing occurs.

T6.   The parabola $y = ax^2 + 19x$, where a is an integer, passes through two lattice points in quadrant I whose ordinates [y-coordinates] are primes. Compute the (x and y) coordinates of both of those points.

T7.   "Lewis and Carol travel together on a road from A to B, then return on the same road, with the entire trip taking 3 hours. Sometimes that road goes uphill, sometimes downhill, and sometimes it is level. When the road goes uphill, their rate is 40 mph;

downhill their rate is 60 mph; on level road their rate is x mph."

Even if you were given a numerical value for x, the distance from A to B would (in most cases) not be uniquely determined. But there is one value for x that *would* determine that distance uniquely. Compute this value of x. [Note: Uphill going is downhill returning!]

T8.   A circle is inscribed in triangle $A_0B_0C_0$, touching its sides at points A_1, B_1, and C_1.

A circle is inscribed in triangle $A_1B_1C_1$, touching its sides at points A_2, B_2, and C_2.

This process is continued until we get triangle $A_nB_nC_n$, *all* of whose angles are within $1°$ of the angles of an equilateral triangle.

Compute the smallest value of n for which this *must* occur [regardless of the size of the angles of triangle $A_0B_0C_0$].

T9.   For what real value of N does the *range* of the function

$$y = f(x) = \frac{4x^2 + Nx + N}{x + 1},$$

where x is real [and $x \neq -1$], consist of all the real numbers except for a single interval of the form $-L < y < L$?

T10.   Point P is inside a rectangular box. The distances from point P to four of the vertices of the box are 1, 2, 3, and 4. If the distance from P to another vertex is greater than 5, find that distance.

Individual Questions

I1.   The usual coloring pattern on an 8×8 checkerboard is changed so that 20 unit squares are now colored red, and the rest are colored white. When the board is folded in half along a line parallel to one edge of the board, exactly seven *pairs* of red unit squares coincide. Compute the number of *pairs* of white unit squares that coincide.

I2. Rectangle *PQRS* is inscrib-
     ed in rectangle *ABCD*, as
     shown. If $DR = 3$, $RP = 13$,
     and $PA = 8$, compute the
     area of rectangle *ABCD*.

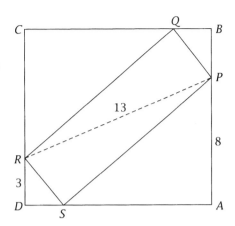

I3. (In this problem, the brackets represent the Greatest Integer
     Function.) Compute $\left[\sqrt{n^2 - 10n + 29}\right]$ when $n = 19941994$.

I4. Semicircles are drawn on two
     sides of square *ABCD*, as shown.
     Point *E* is the center of the
     square, and $\overline{QAP}$ is a line
     segment with $QA = 7$ and
     $AP = 23$. Compute *AE*.

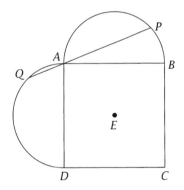

I5. In the addition below, each letter represents a different digit.
     Compute the digit that J represents.

$$
\begin{array}{r}
ABC \\
DEF \\
+\ GHI \\
\hline
1J32
\end{array}
$$

I6. Regular decagon $P_1 P_2 \ldots P_{10}$ is drawn in the coordinate plane,
     with P_1 at $(1, 0)$ and P_6 at $(3, 0)$. If P_n is the point (x_n, y_n),
     compute the numerical value of the product

$$(x_1 + y_1 i)(x_2 + y_2 i)(x_3 + y_3 i) \cdots (x_{10} + y_{10} i).$$

I7. A tangent from the point $(2 \cdot 1994, 2 \cdot 1994)$ to the circle $x^2 +
     y^2 = 1994^2$ touches the circle at the point (a, b). Compute $a + b$.

I8.   Silas once had between 30 and 35 special coins, each marked
       with a different "value". These values were successive powers
       of 2, namely: $1, 2, 4, 8, \ldots$. Some of these coins were then lost.
       The total value of the lost coins was exactly 1/5 of the total value
       of all the original coins. Compute the number of lost coins.

Relay #1

R1-1. Compute the smallest positive integer n such that the product
      $(13)(19)(n)$ is also the product of three *consecutive* integers.

R1-2. Let T = TNYWR, and let $N = T/111$.

      Compute the largest odd divisor of $2^N + 4^N + 8^N$.

R1-3. Let T = TNYWR.

      Compute the largest integer n such that

      $$1(1!) + 2(2!) + 3(3!) + \cdots + n(n!) < T! .$$

Relay #2

R2-1. The integer n is 124 less than one perfect square and 56 less
      than another perfect square. Compute n.

R2-2. Let T = TNYWR, and let $d = T/50$.

      In triangle ABC, median $BM = 29$. A perpendicular from C to
      ray $\overrightarrow{BM}$ meets $\overrightarrow{BM}$ at R. If $CR = d$, compute the area of triangle
      ABC.

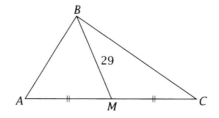

R2-3. Let T = TNYWR.

The line
$$5x + 2y = 1994$$

does not intersect the circle $x^2 + y^2 = T$. Compute the coordinates of the point on the circle that is closest to the line. [Be sure to give your answer in the form of an ordered pair.]

NYSML PROBLEMS

1989
New York State
Mathematics League

Power Question—Some Series

In this problem, brackets represent the Greatest Integer Function, and *n will always represent a positive integer.* You are reminded that calculators are not to be used in solving these problems.

We define $S_n = [\frac{n}{1}]+[\frac{n}{2}]+[\frac{n}{3}]+ \cdots + [\frac{n}{n}]$ and $S_0 = 0$.

I. Compute S_n for $n = 1, 2, 3, 4, 5, 6$, and 7.

II. A. Let a be a positive integer. Show that $[\frac{n}{a}]= [\frac{n-1}{a}]$ if $a \nmid n$, but $[\frac{n}{a}]= [\frac{n-1}{a}]+1$ if $a|n$. (Note: $a|n$ means "a divides n"; thus n is an integer multiple of a.)

B. Let $\tau(n)$ represent the number of (positive integer) divisors of n. For example, since 6 has four divisors $(1, 2, 3,$ and $6)$, $\tau(6)= 4$. Show that $S_n = S_{n-1} + \tau(n)$.

C. For $n > 1$, $\tau(n)\geq 2$ so $S_n \geq S_{n-1} + 2$. Use this fact to prove that $S_n \geq 2n - 1$ (for *all* positive integers n).

D. Suppose you have an extensive table of successive values of S_n for large n. Explain how these values can be used to determine, for values of n within the table, whether

   1. n is a prime number;
   2. n is a perfect square.

JUSTIFY EACH ANSWER.

III.   Let $H_n = 1 + \frac{1}{2} + \frac{1}{3} + \cdots + \frac{1}{n}$.

  A. Note that $(1)+(\frac{1}{2}+\frac{1}{3})+(\frac{1}{4}+\frac{1}{5}+\frac{1}{6}+\frac{1}{7})< 1+1+1$, so $H_7 < 3$. Show that if $n = 2^a - 1$, where a is a positive integer, then $H_n \leq a$.

  B. Show that $n(H_n - 1)< S_n \leq n \cdot H_n$.

  C. Show that $S_{1000} < 10000$.

Team Questions

T1.   Compute the greatest integer that *must* divide $n^3(n^2-1)(n^2-4)$ for every positive integer n.

T2.   The sequence $\frac{1}{2}, \frac{5}{3}, \frac{11}{8}, \frac{27}{19}, \ldots$ is formed as follows: each denominator is the sum of the numerator and denominator of the previous term; each numerator is the sum of its own denominator and the previous denominator. The successive terms are approaching the real number n as a limit. Compute n.

T3.   Compute the area of the circle that passes through all the intersection points of $4x^2 + 11y^2 = 29$ and $x^2 - 6y^2 = 6$.

T4.   If the 2-digit number n is increased or decreased by the positive integer k, the digital sum of each of the resulting numbers is the same as that of n. If n is increased or decreased by $2k$, the digital sums of each of the resulting (positive) numbers is different from that of n. If $k < 17$, compute n.

T5.   The altitude to the hypotenuse of a right triangle cuts it into segments of lengths p and q, $p < q$. If that altitude is $1/4$ the hypotenuse, then p/q will equal $a - b\sqrt{3}$. Compute the ordered pair of positive integers (a,b).

T6.   The vertices of triangle ABC are the centers of three circles that are mutually tangent externally. If $\sin A : \sin B : \sin C = 2 : 3 : 4$, then the radii of the circles, from largest to smallest, are in the ratio $p : q : s$. Compute the ordered triple (p,q,s) where $p, q,$ and s have no common factor greater than 1.

T7.   Let z be such that $z^7 = 1$ and $z \neq 1$. Compute the numerical value of
$$z^{10} + \frac{1}{z^{10}} + z^{30} + \frac{1}{z^{30}} + z^{50} + \frac{1}{z^{50}}.$$

T8.   We have an $n \times n$ "checkerboard" of boxes. The integers from 1 through n^2 are entered in the successive boxes, with the first n integers in row one (consecutively), the next n integers in row two, etc. [EXAMPLE: For $n = 3$ we would have

1	2	3
4	5	6
7	8	9

.]

Suppose we choose n of these integers in such a way that no two of them are in the same row or column. Regardless of how this choice is made, it turns out that the sum is dependent only on the value of n. In fact, this sum is expressible as a *polynomial* in n. What is this polynomial?

T9.   (Note: Assume that all sets mentioned here are subsets of a set I. If X represents a set of elements, then X' represents all elements of I that are *not* in X.)

Let A, B, C, D, and E represent five sets that intersect one another. If the expression

$$[[(B \cap C) \cup (A \cap E)] \cap [(B \cap C) \cup A']]$$
$$\cup [[(C \cap D') \cup (A \cap E')] \cap [(C \cap D') \cup A']]$$
$$\cup [(B' \cup C)' \cup (C \cup D)']$$

is simplified as much as possible, the result is equal to $Y \cup Z'$, where Y and Z belong to $\{A, B, C, D, E\}$. Find the ordered pair (Y, Z).

T10. If $(\sin 1°)(\sin 3°)(\sin 5°) \cdots (\sin 87°)(\sin 89°) = \frac{1}{2^n}$, compute the rational number n.

Individual Questions

I1.   Points P and Q are on circle O, and chord $\overline{PQ}$ is drawn. A second circle is drawn with diameter $\overline{OP}$, crossing the chord at point S. If $OP = 7$ and $PQ = 12$, compute PS.

I2. Compute the positive integer x such that

$$4x^3 - 41x^2 + 10x = 1989.$$

I3. A quadrilateral is circumscribed about a circle. If three sides of the quadrilateral are 17, 18, and 21, not necessarily in that order, compute the smallest possible value for the fourth side.

I4. If $x = 1989(a - b), y = 1989(b - c)$, and $z = 1989(c - a)$, compute the numerical value of

$$\frac{x^2 + y^2 + z^2}{xy + yz + xz},$$

given that $xy + yz + xz \neq 0$.

I5. The sequence $1,2,4,5,10,11,22,23,46,47,\ldots$ is formed as follows:

Start with the number 1

$$\begin{cases} \text{Add one to get 2} \\ \text{Double that to get 4} \end{cases}$$

$$\begin{cases} \text{Add one to get 5} \\ \text{Double that to get 10} \end{cases}$$

etc. [continue increasing by 1, then doubling]. The 100th term will be of the form $3 \cdot 2^k - 1$. Compute k.

I6. Compute the smallest positive angle x, in degrees, such that

$$\tan 4x = \frac{\cos x - \sin x}{\cos x + \sin x}.$$

I7. If each point of the circle $x^2 + y^2 = 25$ is reflected in the point $(4, 1)$, the set of image points satisfies the equation

$$x^2 + ay^2 + bx + cy + d = 0.$$

Compute the ordered quadruple of real numbers (a, b, c, d).

I8. The diagonals of rhombus $ABCD$ are 10 and 4. Rhombus $CDEF$ is drawn in the same plane, with $\overline{DE} \perp \overline{DA}$. Compute the area of rhombus $CDEF$.

Relay #1

R1-1. The positive integer K has n digits, and is equal to $2608n$. Compute K.

R1-2. Let S be the sum of the digits of TNYWR, and let $T = S - 5$.

Compute the sum of the digits when the number 1989^T is expanded and written in base 1,988.

R1-3. Let $R =$ TNYWR, and let $T = 5(R - 1)$.

We have seven slips of paper, each containing a different integer from 1 through 7. We randomly select k slips (without replacement). If the probability that the k slips contain the integers from 1 through k (in any order) is $1/T$, compute the smallest possible value for k.

R1-4. Let $T =$ TNYWR, and let $k = T + 2$.

In a right triangle, the larger acute angle, θ, is k times the angle between the altitude and median to the hypotenuse. Compute the number of degrees in θ.

R1-5. Let $T =$ TNYWR, and let $P = \frac{T}{10} + 1$.

A man has dollar bills in each of three pockets. One pocket has P dollars; another pocket has $1/6$ of all the bills; the third pocket has $k/5$ of all the bills, k an integer from 1 through 5 inclusive. Compute the number of bills he has all together.

Relay #2

R2-1. The 4-digit number ABBA is a multiple of 7. Compute the largest possible value for A + B.

R2-2. Let $T =$ TNYWR, and let $k = T/4$.

A line goes through the points $(k, \sqrt{3})$ and $(p, 5\sqrt{3})$. If the line makes a $60°$ angle with (the positive direction of) the x-axis, compute p.

R2-3. Let a = TNYWR, which will be positive.

The points $A(a, a), B(-b, b)$, and $C(0, 0)$ form a triangle in which angle $BAC = 45°$. Compute the area of this triangle.

R2-4. Let T = TNYWR, and let $K = T/4$.

A car service charges 25¢ per 1/4 mile traveled. If a 20 minute ride costs K dollars, compute the average speed of the car for that trip (in mph).

R2-5. Let T = TNYWR, and let $k = T/6$.

The translation $T_1: (x, y) \rightarrow (x+2, y+3)$ followed by the dilation $D_1: (x, y) \rightarrow (kx, ky)$ is equivalent to the dilation $D_2: (x, y) \rightarrow (kx, ky)$ followed by the translation $T_2: (x, y) \rightarrow (x + c, y + d)$. Compute the ordered pair (c, d).

1990
New York State
Mathematics League

Power Question—A Spiral of Lattice Points

Let the lattice points in the plane be ordered in the "box-spiral" manner indicated in the diagram: P_0 is $(0,0)$, P_1 is $(0,1)$, P_2 is $(-1,1)$, P_3 is $(-1,0)$, etc.

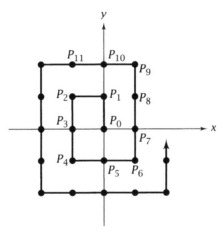

I. A. If n is a positive integer and P_k is the point indicated below, express k as a function of n:
    1. $(-n, -n)$ 2. $(n, n+1)$ 3. $(-n, n)$ 4. $(n, -n)$

   B. Compute the coordinates of each point below:
    1. P_{100} 2. P_{225} 3. P_{380} 4. P_{420}

   C. 1. Compute the coordinates of P_{1000}.
      2. Compute k if P_k is the point $(10, -20)$.

II.   Show all work for each of the following problems.

A.   The points P_0, P_2, and P_8 lie on the parabola $y = x^2$. There are an infinite number of other values of k for which P_k lies on this parabola; all these other values (and only these values) are produced by the formula $k = an^4 + bn^2 \pm n$, where a and b are fixed constants, and n takes on all integer values greater than 1. Compute the ordered pair of integers (a, b).

B.   The points P_3, P_5, and P_7 each lie on a coordinate axis. Show that P_k does *not* lie on a coordinate axis for any other prime value of k.

C.   Find all values of k for which the length of segment $\overline{P_k P_{2k}}$ is 1 unit.

Team Questions

T1.   [Note: A "unit fraction" is a fraction of the form $\frac{1}{n}$, where n is a positive integer.]

If $x^2 - y^2 = x - y$, where $x > y$ and y is a unit fraction, compute the smallest possible value for x.

T2.   The arc shown is part of a circle. Which of the following *must* be true (indicate the letter preceding *each* correct answer):

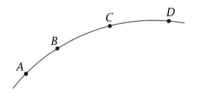

(a)   The perpendicular bisectors of $\overline{AB}, \overline{BC}$, and $\overline{CD}$ are concurrent (all go through the same point).

(b)   If $\overline{AC}$ and $\overline{BD}$ intersect at P, then $(AP)(PC) = (BP)(PD)$.

(c) $\angle ABD = \angle ACD$.

(d) $\angle ABC$ and $\angle ADC$ are supplementary.

(e) $\overarc{AB} : \overarc{CD} = \overline{AB} : \overline{CD}$.

T3.   If $a = \log 9$ and $b = \log 16$, compute $4^{a/b} + 3^{b/a}$.

T4.   Let "reversed dates" be dates in which the month and day are interchanged [for example, dates 2/10 (February 10) and 10/2 (October 2)]. Find the date for which the reversed date is exactly 60 days later. Give your answer in the form (m, d), where m is the number of the month and d is the number of the day.

T5.   The 4-digit number ABCD is a perfect square, and the 2-digit number CD is one less than the 2-digit number AB. Compute the number ABCD.

T6.   A sequence $\langle S_n \rangle$ is defined as follows: $S_1 = 1, S_2 = 1,$

$$S_n = \frac{S_{n-2} \cdot S_{n-1}}{S_{n-2} + S_{n-1}} \text{ for } n > 2.$$

Compute S_{12}.

T7.   Compute the smallest positive integer k such that $2^{24} + k$ is divisible by 127.

T8.   Compute all positive integer values of $n, 1 < n < 100$, such that $\binom{n}{2}$ is a perfect square.

T9.   In convex quadrilateral $ABCD$, $AB = 15, BC = 7, CD = 24$, $AD = 20$, and angle $A = 90°$. Compute AC.

T10.   Let the "parts" of a triangle be its three sides and three angles. Five parts of triangle ABC are congruent to five parts of triangle DEF, yet the triangles are not congruent. If the sides of *both* triangles are integers, compute the smallest possible value for the perimeter of triangle ABC.

Individual Questions

I1.   When multiplied out, 15! is equal to 130767A368000. Compute the missing digit A.

I2.   Each vertex of a hexagon is assigned an ordered pair of numbers, as shown in the diagram. For each vertex, the "second

number" is the arithmetic average (mean) of the "first numbers"
of the two vertices adjacent to it. [For example, $10 = (a + c)/2$.]
Compute a.

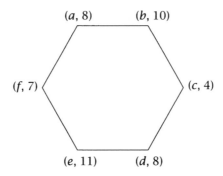

I3.   The expressions $a \cdot b, a/b, a + b$, and $a - b$ each represent a real
       number, and three of them are equal. Compute the two ordered
       pairs of real numbers (a, b) for which this is true.

I4.   The vertices of triangle ABC are the points $A(0, 6), B(12, 0)$, and
       $C(0, 0)$. A line through the point $(3, 0)$ bisects the area of the
       triangle. Compute the slope of this line.

I5.   The curve $y = \sin x$ cuts the line whose equation is $y = \sin 70°$
       into segments having the successive ratios

$$\ldots p : q : p : q : \ldots ,$$

       with $p < q$. Compute the ordered pair of relatively prime posi-
       tive integers (p, q).

I6.   The bases of a trapezoid are 3 and 12, and one leg is 2. If one
       diagonal is 12, compute the length of the other diagonal.

I7.   [Note: The "reflection of point P in line ℓ" is a point P' (called
       the image of P) such that ℓ is the perpendicular bisector of $\overline{PP'}$.
       The reflection of a set of points is the set of their images.]

       The parabola $y = x^2$ is reflected in the line $y = 3$, producing a
       new parabola. This new parabola is reflected in the line $x = 2$,
       producing the parabola $y = -x^2 + bx + c$. Compute the ordered
       pair of numbers (b, c).

I8.   [Note: The product of k consecutive positive integers cannot be a perfect square if $k > 1$.]

If a and b are integers, $20 < a < b < 40$, and

$$N = [a! + (a + 1)! + (a + 2)!][b! + (b + 1)! + (b + 2)!],$$

compute all values of a that make N a perfect square.

Relay #1

R1-1. The square of the sum of the digits of a 2-digit number, decreased by the sum of the squares of the digits, is a perfect square. Compute the largest such 2-digit number.

R1-2. Let T = TNYWR, and let $R = T/49$.

In the diagram, minor arcs $\overset{\frown}{AB}$ and $\overset{\frown}{CB}$ each are 1/4 of a circle of radius R, and are tangent at B. Arc $\overset{\frown}{ADC}$ is a semicircle of radius R. Compute the enclosed area shown.

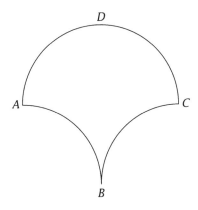

R1-3. Let A = TNYWR.

If the 3-digit numbers ABC and CBA each leave the same remainder when divided by 7, and A ≠ C, compute the value of the digit C.

Relay #2

R2-1. Compute the area of the smallest square that goes through the points (0,0) and (4,0).

R2-2. Let T = TNYWR, and let $K = T - 5$.

The positive integer n is even, and all its divisors (except n itself) divide $n/2$. Compute the largest K-digit number n with this property.

R2-3. Let N = TNYWR, and let K be the sum of the digits of N.

Two secants are drawn to a circle from an outside point, intercepting arcs (between them) of lengths $K\pi$ and 2π. If the angle between the secants is 30°, compute the radius of the circle.

1991
New York State
Mathematics League

Power Question—Sums of Consecutive Integers

Let $T(N)$ be the number of ways to represent a positive integer N as a sum of one or more consecutive positive integers (in increasing order). In this problem, we use the phrase "one consecutive integer" to refer to a single-term representation of N. For example: $49 = 4 + 5 + 6 + 7 + 8 + 9 + 10$, $49 = 24 + 25$, and $49 = 49$, so $T(49) = 3$.

I.   In each case, find $T(N)$ by actually listing all the representations of N as a sum of consecutive positive integers (as illustrated in the example above):

    (a) $T(3), T(7)$;

    (b) $T(21), T(42)$;

    (c) $T(9), T(27)$.

II. (a) The smallest square that is the sum of three consecutive positive integers is 9. Find the next two higher such squares.

    (b) Show that no cube is the sum of eight consecutive positive integers.

    (c) Determine, with proof, all values of k (greater than 1) for which the sum of k consecutive positive integers must be divisible by k.

III.   Prove each of the following, where p and q represent distinct odd primes, and a and b represent positive integers:

(a) $T(p) = 2$;

(b) $T(2^a) = 1$;

(c) $T(p^a) = a + 1$;

(d) $T(p^a \cdot q^b) = T(p^a) \cdot T(q^b)$.

[Note: 1. The result of III(d) can be similarly extended to any number of distinct odd primes.

2. It can also be shown that $T(2^a N) = T(N)$.]

IV.   (a) Compute $T(15!)$. (No work need be shown.)

(b) Find the smallest positive integer N such that $T(N) = 12$. Show your work.

(c) Let 510 be expressed as the sum of k consecutive positive integers. Compute the smallest of these integers if k is as large as possible. Show your work.

Team Questions

T1.   If $A(3, 4)$ and $C(7, 10)$ are opposite vertices of rectangle $ABCD$, then vertices B and D *must* lie on the circle

$$x^2 + y^2 - px - qy + s = 0.$$

Compute the ordered triple of real numbers (p, q, s).

T2.   A side of regular polygon I is an integer, and is equal to a side of regular polygon II. An angle of I is the supplement of an angle of II. If the perimeter of one of these polygons is 15, compute the perimeter of the other. [There is only one answer!]

T3.   In a certain city, a taxi charges 20¢ *per 1/5 mile* traveled when moving faster than x mph. It charges 15¢ *per minute* when moving slower than x mph. At x mph, both methods of charging produce the same cost to the rider. Compute x.

T4.   Starting at the origin of a rectangular coordinate system, we move in the following way, always going to the right, and in a counterclockwise direction: First we go at a $1°$ angle [with the horizontal] for $(\cos 1°)$ units. From there we go at a $2°$ angle [with the horizontal] for $(\cos 2°)$ units; similarly, we go from there at a $3°$ angle for $(\cos 3°)$ units; and so on; finally we go at a $90°$ angle for $(\cos 90°)$ units. Compute the x-coordinate of the final point.

T5.   If
$$\binom{1991}{991} + \binom{1991}{992} = \binom{1992}{x}$$
and $x > 996$, compute x.

T6.   A one-to-one mapping (function) is made from the set $S = \{1, 2, 3, 4, 5\}$ onto itself subject to the following two restrictions:

1.   If $n \in S$, n does *not* map to $n - 1$, to n, or to $n + 1$.

2.   If $n \in S$ and n maps to r, then r does *not* map to n or to $n + 1$.

What does the number 3 map to?

T7.   [Note: A palindrome is a positive integer that reads backwards the same as it reads forwards. For example: 67276.]

Let S be the set of all 15-digit positive integers. An integer is chosen at random from S. The probability that it is a palindrome is $\frac{1}{10^k}$. Compute k.

T8.   Two circles have radii 1 and 7, and one of their common internal tangents is perpendicular to a common external tangent. Compute the distance between their centers.

T9.   [For all complex numbers $a + bi$, where a and b are real, we define $|a + bi| = \sqrt{a^2 + b^2}$. For example, $|3 - 4i| = 5$.]

Let z be the complex number $x + yi$, where x and y are real variables. In the xy-plane, if the graph of $|z - 3| = 2 \cdot |z + 3|$ intersects the graph of $|z| = k$ in exactly one point, compute the value of k for which $0 < k < 8$.

T10.   In triangle ABC, $AB = AC$ and cos $\sphericalangle BAC = 1/3$. If points P and Q trisect $\overline{BC}$, compute cos $\sphericalangle PAQ$.

Individual Questions

I1.   Let set $S = \{11, 13, 14, 15, 17, 27, 28, 29, 36, 51\}$. Five distinct integers are chosen from the set S. Their product is 2,137,590. Compute their sum.

I2.   Let $f(x) = x^2 + bx + 9$ and $g(x) = x^2 + dx + e$. If $f(x) = 0$ has roots r and s, and $g(x) = 0$ has roots $-r$ and $-s$, compute the two roots of $f(x) + g(x) = 0$.

I3.   [Note: A palindrome is a positive integer that reads backwards the same as it reads forwards. For example: 67276.]

       John thought he had added together every 2-digit positive integer, and the sum he got was a palindrome. Unfortunately, he had left one number out. What number had been omitted?

I4.   In a convex polygon of n sides, one interior angle contains $x°$, while each of the remaining $n - 1$ interior angles contains $133°$. Compute all four possible values for x.

I5.   The perimeter of parallelogram $ABCD$ is 40, and its altitudes are 4 and 7. Compute sin A.

I6.   If the set of simultaneous equations

$$x + y + z = 2$$
$$2x + 4y + 3z = 5$$
$$ax + by + 2z = 9$$

       is satisfied by an infinite number of real triples (x, y, z), compute the ordered pair of real numbers (a, b).

I7.   When one vertex of a paper rectangle is folded onto the center of the rectangle, the crease [fold] passes through another vertex of the rectangle. Compute the ratio of the longest side of the rectangle to the shortest side.

I8.   The number 26! ends in a string of 0's. Let N be the integer
        that remains when all those finals 0's are deleted [removed].
        Compute the largest integer k such that 12^k is a divisor of N.

Relay #1

R1-1. Angles A and B are complementary. If $\sin 2A = 1/4$, compute
      $\sin 2B$.

R1-2. Let T = TNYWR and let $N = 12T$.

      How many N-digit (positive) integers do not contain the digits
      1 or 9?

R1-3. Let T = TNYWR and let $P = T/16$.

      In triangle ABC, two tangent circles are drawn, with tangent
      points at D, E, F, G, H, and J, as shown. If $DE = 3$, $CF = 5$, and
      the perimeter of triangle ABC is P, compute AB.

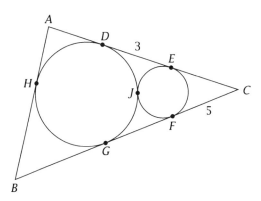

Relay #2

R2-1. (Note: In this problem, the brackets represent the Greatest In-
      teger Function.)

      Compute x if $[x] \cdot x = 11$.

R2-2. Let T = TNYWR and let $L = 3T$.

A rectangle is inscribed in an isosceles right triangle, as shown. If each leg of the triangle is L, compute the perimeter of the rectangle.

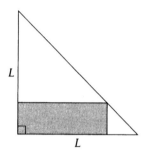

R2-3. Let T = TNYWR and let $N = T - 13$.

Two rectangles are inscribed in the same circle. One has dimensions $3 \times h$, and the other has dimensions $N \times k$. If $h + k = 24$, compute $h - k$.

1992
New York State
Mathematics League

Power Question—Square Billiards

I. Square $ABCD$ is positioned in the coordinate plane as shown in figure 1. A "ball" [point] travels a path that begins at corner A [the vertices of square $ABCD$ will be called corners], goes to a point P_1 on $\overline{DC}$, then reflects off that side to some point P_2 on another side, and continues to reflect off the sides of the square. ["Reflection" implies that the path makes congruent angles with the side of the square off of which it reflects.] The path terminates if it reaches one of the corners of the square. (See for example figures 2 and 3.)

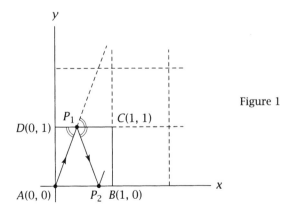

Figure 1

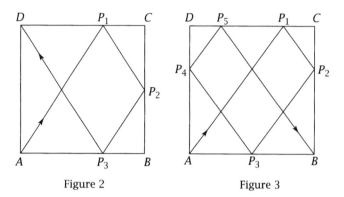

Figure 2   Figure 3

Each segment $\overline{P_iP_{i+1}}$ of the broken-line path will be called a "leg" of the path. Let T represent the total length of the path; let L represent the number of legs in the path; let a represent the length DP_1.

A. In figure 1, let $a = 2/5$.

    1. Find the coordinates of point J, the lattice point on $\overrightarrow{AP_1}$ that is closest to A (other than A itself).

    2. Each lattice point in the plane is the image of one of the vertices of square $ABCD$ under successive reflections of the square about its sides. Which corner of square $ABCD$ does point J correspond to? [This corner is the terminal point of the path.]

    3. Compute T and L.

B. Let $a = q/r$, where q and r are relatively prime positive integers and $q/r < 1$.

    1. Express T in terms of q and r. Express L in terms of q and r.

    2.   (a) Since a is rational, the path must terminate. Explain, in terms of q and r, how to determine the corner [$A, B, C,$ or D] at which the path ends, including the reason why no path can terminate at corner A.

        (b) Show that, if L is odd, the path must end at corner C.

        (c) Show that, if T is rational, the path cannot terminate at corner C.

3. (a) If $L = 17$, compute all possible values for a.
   (b) If $T = \sqrt{65}$, find all possible values for L and which corner the path ends at in each case.

4. (a) For a given value of L, there may be many possible positions for P_1. Of these positions, show that T is a minimum when P_1 is as close to corner C as possible.
   (b) Consider the shortest path for which $L = 100$. The corner at which it ends is also P_{100}.
      (1) Compute the coordinates of P_{99}.
      (2) Compute the coordinates of P_{22}.

II. In this section, the ball reflects off the sides of *rectangle ABCD*, with coordinates $A(0,0), B(2,0), C(2,1)$, and $D(0,1)$. The rules of reflection are the same as in section I. Once again, the ball always starts at corner A and goes first to point P_1 on $\overline{DC}$. Here $a = DP_1 = q/r$, where q and r are relatively prime positive integers and $q/r < 2$.

Prove that the corner at which the path ends is completely determined by q; be sure to show how to determine which corner is the final one in each case, including the reason why no path can terminate at corner A.

III. In this section, the ball reflects off the sides of equilateral triangle ABC, of side 1. The rules of reflection are the same as in section I. The ball starts at corner A and goes first to point P_1 on $\overline{BC}$.

If $CP_1 : P_1B = 3 : 5$, compute L and T, and determine at which corner the path terminates.

Team Questions

T1. Two of the altitudes of an acute triangle cut the sides to which they are drawn into segments of lengths 5, 3, 2, and x, as shown. Compute x.

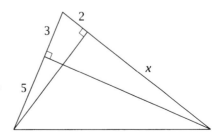

T2. A line with slope -2 is 2 units from the origin. Compute the area of the triangle formed by this line and the coordinate axes.

T3. Compute the smallest positive integer that exactly divides 16! but does *not* divide 14!.

T4. Compute the number of ordered pairs (x, y) with the property that x and y are each 2-digit numbers, $x < y$, and $x \cdot y$ is a 3-digit number whose three digits are identical.

T5. The number $(9^6 + 1)$ is the product of three primes. Compute the largest of these primes.

T6. There are two 4-digit numbers, ABCA, with the property that AB is a prime, BC is a square, and CA is the product of a prime and a square that is greater than 1. Compute the larger of these 4-digit numbers.

T7. If $f(x) = |3x - 1|$, compute all values of x for which $f(f(x)) = x$.

T8. In a three-dimensional rectangular coordinate system with origin O, points A, B, and C are on the x-, y-, and z-axes, respectively. If the areas of triangles OAB, OAC, and OBC are 4, 6, and 12, respectively, compute the area of triangle ABC.

T9. Compute the smallest integer n for which $1 + 2 + 3 + 4 + \cdots + n = (n + 1) + (n + 2) + (n + 3) + \cdots + (n + k)$ for some integer $k > 1$.

T10. A convex pentagon is inscribed in a circle. If its sides are $16, 16, 16, 16$, and 6, its area will be $k\sqrt{7}$. Compute the number k.

Individual Questions

I1. If $2(7^2 + 24^2)^5 + 3(15^2 + 20^2)^5 = 5^k$, compute the integer k.

I2. Compute the number of squares *between* 7^4 and 4^7.

I3. Compute the largest prime factor of $3^{12} + 2^{12} - 2 \cdot 6^6$. [Reminder: Calculators may *not* be used.]

I4. The point $A(4, 0)$ is a vertex of regular hexagon $ABCDEF$, whose side is 8 and whose interior lies completely within Quadrant I. If vertex D has coordinates (x, y), compute the ordered pair (x, y).

I5. Right triangle ABC is made of paper. Hypotenuse $\overline{AB} = 36$. Vertex C is folded onto the midpoint of $\overline{AB}$, forming crease $\overline{XY}$ (where points X and Y are on the legs of the triangle). Given that $XY = 20$, compute the area of triangle XYC.

I6. The first three terms of an arithmetic progression are $\tan x$, $\cos x$, and $\sec x$, respectively. If the kth term is $\cot x$, compute k.

I7. Let r be a root of $x^2 + 5x + 7 = 0$. Compute

$$(r - 1)(r + 2)(r + 6)(r + 3).$$

I8. Two circles of radius r are each tangent to the hypotenuse and a leg of a right triangle, and tangent to each other, as shown. If the sides of the triangle are 3, 4, and 5, compute r.

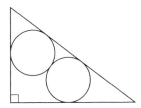

Relay #1

R1-1. Compute $\log 2^{4^2} + \log 5^{2^4}$.

R1-2. Let $T = $ TNYWR and let $D = T/2$.

The point $(1992, D)$ is on a square whose four vertices are on the axes. If the side of the square is equal to $b\sqrt{2}$, compute b.

R1-3. Let T = TNYWR and let $R = \frac{T}{100} + 4$.

For a certain value of n, the expressions $3n^2 + 4n - R$ and $2n^2 + 3n - R + 56$ each equal the same prime, p. Compute the value of p.

Relay #2

R2-1. Two sides of a triangle lie along the x- and y-axes. Compute the area of the triangle if its medians meet at (4,2).

R2-2. Let T = TNYWR and let $R = T/4$.

If $\dfrac{1}{\dfrac{1}{x} + \dfrac{1}{R}} = 6$, compute x.

R2-3. Let T = TNYWR, which will be a positive integer.

Compute the largest integer value of x that makes the expression $(x - T)^2 + 16$ a perfect square.

TIEBREAKERS

ARML AND NYSML Tiebreakers

When ties occurred among top individual scores, tiebreakers were used to decide the final ranking. The order of awards was determined by how quickly a correct answer was submitted. In the following listing, contest and year are indicated in brackets. If more than one tiebreaker was used in any contest, they were given in the order in which they appear here.

1. [NYSML 1983] Let z and $z + 1$ be nth roots of unity, where n is a positive integral multiple of 7. Compute the smallest possible numerical value for $n - z^3$.

2. [NYSML 1983] If $ABCDEFG$ is a regular heptagon and diagonals $\overline{AC}$ and $\overline{BF}$ intersect at P, compute angle APB.

3. [NYSML 1984] If

    $$x^3 + 5x^2 + 3x - 1 = A(x - 1)^3 + B(x - 1)^2 + C(x - 1) + D$$

    is an identity, and A, B, C, and D are constants, compute $B + D$.

4. [ARML 1984] Triangle ABC is inscribed in a circle and $\overline{BP}$ bisects angle ABC. If $AB = 6$, $BC = 8$, and $AC = 7$, compute BP.

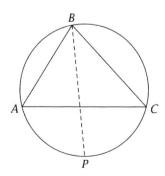

5. [ARML 1984] Compute the maximum value of $\log x + \log y + \log z$ if x, y, and z are positive, and $x + 4y + 16z = 120$.

6. [NYSML 1985] If $A_n = 1 + 3 + 5 + \cdots + (2n - 1)$, for n a positive integer, and $B_n = \log A_1 + \log A_2 + \log A_3 + \cdots + \log A_n$, then $B_6 + B_7 = B_x$. Compute the positive integer x.

7. [ARML 1985] Compute $[(4 + \sqrt{15})^3]$, where the brackets denote the Greatest Integer Function.

8. [ARML 1985] If $\frac{\cos 2x}{\cos x} = 2$, find the value of $\frac{\sin 2x}{\sin x}$.

9. [ARML 1985] If $S_n = 1^3 + 2^3 + 3^3 + \cdots + n^3$, compute

$$\frac{1}{\sqrt{S_1}} + \frac{1}{\sqrt{S_2}} + \frac{1}{\sqrt{S_3}} + \cdots + \frac{1}{\sqrt{S_{1985}}}.$$

10. [ARML 1986] Compute the area bounded by the graph of

$$y^3 - xy^2 - 3y^2 = 4x^2y - 4x^3 - 12x^2.$$

11. [ARML 1986] Two of the three altitudes of a right triangle are of lengths 4 and 5. Compute the longest possible length for the third altitude.

12. [NYSML 1987] Three vertices of a parallelogram are $A(1,3)$, $B(4,8)$, and $C(6,2)$. There are three other points that can be the fourth vertex of the parallelogram. Compute the sum of the abscissas of those three other points.

13. [NYSML 1987] The equation $x^2 + bx + c = 0$ has roots r and s; the equation $x^2 + cx + b = 0$ has roots r and t. If b and c are real but unequal, compute the numerical value of $s + t$.

14. [ARML 1987] The slopes of two lines through the origin are p and q, with $p > q > 0$. The line $y = x$ bisects the angle between those lines. If $p + q = \sqrt{13}$, compute $p - q$.

15. [NYSML 1988] In circle O, diameter $\overline{AOB}$ is extended through B to point P. Tangent segment $\overline{PT}$ is drawn to the circle. If $PT = 9/2$, compute *all* integer values of AB that make BP rational.

16. [NYSML 1988] Compute the numerical value of

$$\left(5^{\log 2}\right)\left(2^{\log 3}\right)\left(2^{\log 6}\right)\left(5^{\log 9}\right).$$

17. [ARML 1988] If x is acute and
$$\tan 2x = \frac{\cos x - \sin x}{\cos x + \sin x},$$
compute the numerical value of $|\tan 4x|$.

18. [NYSML 1989] Compute the largest prime factor of $3^{14} + 3^{13} - 12$.

19. [NYSML 1989] Compute $\log\left((\sqrt{5})^{\sqrt{8}}(\sqrt[3]{2})^{\sqrt{18}}\right)$.

20. [ARML 1989] In the accompanying diagram, the slope of $\overline{AB}$ is m, $m > 1$, and $\overline{AB} \perp \overline{BC}$, $\overline{BC} \perp \overline{CD}$, and $\overline{CD} \perp \overline{DE}$. If $EA = AC$, compute m.

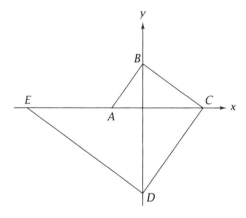

21. [NYSML 1990] Compute the smallest positive integer with the property that the sum of the cubes of its digits is *not* divisible by the sum of its digits.

22. [ARML 1990] Some of the lattice points on the line $7x + 11y = 770$ lie within quadrant I. Compute the average (arithmetic mean) of the x-coordinates of these lattice points.

23. [NYSML 1991] If r and s are the roots of $x^2 + x + 7 = 0$, compute the numerical value of $2r^2 + rs + s^2 + r + 7$.

24. [ARML 1991] Three *distinct positive* integers are in arithmetic progression. If the sum of their cubes is divided by the sum of the three numbers, the quotient is 81. If the numbers are arranged in increasing order, compute the "middle" number.

25. [NYSML 1992] Right triangle OAB, with vertices $O(0,0)$, $A(4,0)$, and $B(4,3)$, is reflected in its hypotenuse. If point C is the image of point A, compute the slope of $\overleftrightarrow{OC}$.

26. [ARML 1992] The points $A(1,0)$ and $B(b,0)$, $b > 1$, are the end-points of a diameter of a circle. A line through the origin, tangent to the circle, has slope $4/3$. Compute b.

27. [ARML 1993] Set $A = \{2, 5, 10, 17, \ldots, n^2 + 1, \ldots\}$ and

    Set $B = \{10001, 10004, 10009, 10016, \ldots, n^2 + 10000, \ldots\}$.

    Compute the number of elements in $A \cap B$.

28. [ARML 1994] Compute the smallest positive integer n, greater than 200, with the property that n is the sum of five consecutive integers, n is the sum of six consecutive integers, and n is the sum of seven consecutive integers.

29. [ARML 1994] Compute the missing digit, A, in the product

    $(9966334) \cdot (9966332) = 99327A93466888.$

ANSWER KEY

Answer Key to ARML AND NYSML Contests, 1989–1994

ARML 1989

T1.	5555	I1.	18	R1-1.	9
T2.	11	I2.	26 [or 26°]	R1-2.	125
T3.	12	I3.	18	R1-3.	4
T4.	2:1 [or 2]	I4.	Any integer angle from		
T5.	13/18		48° through 56°, inclusive	R2-1.	1995
T6.	4	I5.	20	R2-2.	361
T7.	1/4 [or 0.25]	I6.	1700	R2-3.	362
T8.	$\sqrt{50}$ [or $5\sqrt{2}$]	I7.	5120		
T9.	21	I8.	14		
T10.	6				

ARML 1990

T1.	9 or −9 [either answer	I1.	3	R1-1.	660
	is acceptable]	I2.	(5, 15)	R1-2.	165
T2.	(3, 2, 4)	I3.	−5	R1-3.	27
T3.	5	I4.	(7, 3, 1)		
T4.	1/3	I5.	5	R2-1.	6
T5.	24	I6.	8910 [or 8910°]	R2-2.	23
T6.	84	I7.	$(1 + \sqrt{2})/2$	R2-3.	14
T7.	96 and 100	I8.	51, 52, 53		
T8.	$\sqrt{91}$				
T9.	5				
T10.	100 [or 100°]				

ARML 1991

T1.	5	I1.	13	R1-1.	133
T2.	12221	I2.	1328	R1-2.	9
T3.	302	I3.	1/9	R1-3.	6
T4.	$\sqrt[9]{11}$	I4.	$0, \pm 3, \pm 13$		
T5.	3	I5.	8	R2-1.	1/6
T6.	16	I6.	30	R2-2.	2
T7.	11	I7.	8/5 [or 1.6]	R2-3.	$(-3, 6)$
T8.	109	I8.	2240		
T9.	32				
T10.	16				

ARML 1992

T1.	3999960	I1.	28	R1-1.	61
T2.	1	I2.	7	R1-2.	16
T3.	32	I3.	396	R1-3.	$48\sqrt{2}$
T4.	36	I4.	63		
T5.	5	I5.	-2000	R2-1.	121
T6.	64	I6.	10, 50, 54	R2-2.	1/22
T7.	333, 333, 333, 334	I7.	11	R2-3.	$x^{23} - 1$
T8.	31	I8.	5/18 [or 5:18]		
T9.	1/4				
T10.	1/3				

ARML 1993

T1.	50119	I1.	25	R1-1.	100
T2.	3/5 [or 0.6]	I2.	89	R1-2.	7
T3.	7	I3.	-8	R1-3.	7
T4.	4	I4.	$140°, 60°, 160°, 80°$ [any		
T5.	$\sqrt{2}$		order is acceptable]	R2-1.	9
T6.	2657	I5.	$\cos 16° \sin 7°$, $\sin 9°$,	R2-2.	8
T7.	$(5, 6, 11, 11)$		$\sin 16° \cos 7°$, $\cos 67°$	R2-3.	4
T8.	29		[this order is required]		
T9.	144	I6.	3 and 8		
T10.	665	I7.	3		
		I8.	271		

ARML 1994

T1.	10	I1.	19	R1-1.	222
T2.	1/3	I2.	132	R1-2.	21
T3.	1	I3.	19941989	R1-3.	20
T4.	144 or 300 [either answer	I4.	17		
	is acceptable]	I5.	6	R2-1.	200
T5.	$(7,5)$	I6.	1023	R2-2.	116
T6.	$(1,13)$ and $(3,3)$	I7.	997	R2-3.	$(10,4)$
T7.	48	I8.	16		
T8.	7				
T9.	8				
T10.	$\sqrt{27}$ [or $3\sqrt{3}$]				

NYSML 1989

T1.	360	I1.	6	R1-1.	13040
T2.	$\sqrt{2}$	I2.	13	R1-2.	8
T3.	7π	I3.	14	R1-3.	3
T4.	88	I4.	-2	R1-4.	50
T5.	$(7,4)$	I5.	49	R1-5.	180
T6.	$(5,3,1)$	I6.	9 [or 9°]		
T7.	-1	I7.	$(1,-16,-4,43)$	R2-1.	16
T8.	$\frac{n^3}{2}+\frac{n}{2}$ [or $\frac{1}{2}n^3+\frac{1}{2}n$	I8.	21	R2-2.	8
	or $n(n^2+1)/2$]			R2-3.	64
T9.	(B,D)			R2-4.	48
T10.	$89/2$ [or $44\,^{1}/_{2}$ or 44.5]			R2-5.	$(16,24)$

NYSML 1990

T1.	2/3	I1.	4	R1-1.	98
T2.	a,b,c,d [all four	I2.	9	R1-2.	8
	required]	I3.	$(1/2,-1)$ and	R1-3.	1
T3.	7		$(-1/2,-1)$		
T4.	$(7,9)$	I4.	4	R2-1.	8
T5.	8281	I5.	$(1,8)$	R2-2.	512
T6.	1/144	I6.	$\sqrt{14}$	R2-3.	18
T7.	119	I7.	$(8,-10)$		
T8.	2, 9, 50	I8.	24 and 35		
T9.	20				
T10.	38				

NYSML 1991

T1.	$(10, 14, 61)$	I1.	98	R1-1.	1/4
T2.	30	I2.	$\pm 3i$	R1-2.	448
T3.	9	I3.	21	R1-3.	6
T4.	$89/2$ [or $44^1/_2$ or 44.5]	I4.	8, 55, 102, 149		
T5.	1000	I5.	11/20	R2-1.	11/3
T6.	5	I6.	$(7, -3)$	R2-2.	22
T7.	7	I7.	$\sqrt{3}$	R2-3.	3
T8.	10	I8.	8		
T9.	1				
T10.	17/19				

NYSML 1992

T1.	10	I1.	21	R1-1.	16
T2.	5	I2.	78	R1-2.	2000
T3.	125 [or 5^3]	I3.	19	R1-3.	151
T4.	7	I4.	$(12, 8\sqrt{3})$		
T5.	6481	I5.	90	R2-1.	36
T6.	8368	I6.	5	R2-2.	18
T7.	1/4, 1/5, 2/5, 1/2	I7.	13	R2-3.	21
T8.	14	I8.	5/7		
T9.	14				
T10.	123				

TIEBREAKERS

1.	41	11.	20/3	21.	112
2.	$(720/7)°$	12.	11	22.	55
3.	16	13.	-1	23.	-6
4.	8	14.	3	24.	7
5.	3	15.	40 and 12	25.	24/7
6.	10	16.	18	26.	9
7.	1207	17.	$\sqrt{3}$	27.	6
8.	$1 - \sqrt{3}$	18.	73	28.	315
9.	1985/993	19.	$\sqrt{2}$	29.	7
10.	6	20.	$\sqrt{2}$		

SOLUTIONS

1989 American Regions Mathematics League Solutions

Power Question

I.   A. $(7, 24, 25)$ and $(15, 20, 25)$ [which is five times the sides of $(3, 4, 5)$].

     B. $(35, 120, 125)$, $(75, 100, 125)$, and $(44, 117, 125)$. The first two come from the $(7, 24, 25)$ and $(3, 4, 5)$ triangles. A general approach would be to use the fact that the expressions $k(m^2 - n^2)$, $k(2mn)$, and $k(m^2 + n^2)$, where k, m, and n are positive integers with $m > n$, produce all Pythagorean triplets. Setting $m^2 + n^2 = 125$ leads to $m = 10$, $n = 5$ [producing $(75, 100, 125)$] or $m = 11$, $n = 2$ [producing $(44, 117, 125)$]; setting $m^2 + n^2 = 25$ leads to $m = 4$, $n = 3$ [producing $(7, 24, 25)$, for which we then use $k = 5$].

II. A. Ptolemy's Theorem produces $FG = 7/5$. The answer is $(15, 7, 15, 25)$ [in any order].

     B. Using sides $a, x, a, 25$ (each diagonal is $\sqrt{625 - a^2}$) leads to $x = 25 - 2a^2/25$. Positive integral x's come from $a = 5, 10$, or 15. The last leads to the solution in IIA. The other possibilities are $(5, 23, 5, 25)$ OR $(10, 17, 10, 25)$ [either answer, in any order, is acceptable].

     C. Apply the theorem given in part I, for any appropriate d, to find $n - 2$ $P3$'s of hypotenuse d^{n-2}. Build these triangles in a semicircle of diameter d^{n-2}. Connecting successive

points on the semicircle produces an n-gon. Successive
applications of Ptolemy's Theorem to find each side of the
n-gon shows each must be rational. Multiplying all sides by
the least common denominator involved produces a Pn.

III. A. On diameter $\overline{AD}$, draw the $P4$ $ABCD$, with $AB = a$, $BC = b$,
        $CD = c$, $AD = d$, $BD = e$, and angle $BCD = \theta$. The Law of
        Cosines shows that $d^2 = a^2 + e^2 = a^2 + b^2 + c^2 - 2bc \cos \theta$;
        since θ must be obtuse, $\cos \theta$ is negative, so d^2 is greater
        than $a^2 + b^2 + c^2$. Note that this easily extends to any Pn.

      B. Using the $P4$ described in solution IIIA, with $AC = f$,
        Ptolemy's Theorem yields

$$bd + ac = ef = \sqrt{(d^2 - a^2)(d^2 - c^2)}.$$

        Squaring both sides, simplifying, and dividing each term
        by d produces $b^2 d + 2abc = d^3 - a^2 d - c^2 d$. Since all are
        integers, d must divide $2abc$. If d is a prime greater than
        2, it must divide (at least) one of the a, b, c. If $d|a$, for
        example, then $a \geq d$, which is impossible. Therefore d is
        composite or equal to 2; therefore d is composite.

      C1. (1) Using the $P4$ described in solution IIIB, we first show that
        its area must be rational: The area of triangle $ABD = \frac{1}{2}ae$,
        which is integral, since one of the legs must be even (see so-
        lution IB); the area of triangle $BCD = \frac{1}{2}bc \sin \theta$, which must
        be rational since $\sin \theta = e/d$ (by the extended Law of Sines);
        thus the area of the $P4$ is rational. (2) We next show that
        the perimeter of the $P4$ must be even: We first note that all
        primitive Pythagorean triples, being generated by $m^2 - n^2$,
        $2mn$, and $m^2 + n^2$ where m and n are of opposite pari-
        ties, must yield an odd hypotenuse and exactly one even
        leg; if a Pythagorean triple has an even hypotenuse, each
        leg must have *at least* the same degree of evenness as the
        hypotenuse. Now by Ptolemy's Theorem, $b = (ef - ac)/d$,
        and we are given that this is integral. There are now two ba-
        sic possibilities — d can be even [then both ef and ac will
        be of a higher degree of evenness, making b even and the
        perimeter even] or d can be odd [then either e and f are
        even while a and c are odd (making b odd) OR e and f
        are odd while a and c are even (making b odd) OR e and
        f are of opposite parities, as are a and c (making b even); in

each of these situations, the perimeter will be even]. Thus the perimeter is even in every case.

(3) Finally, using s for the semiperimeter, Brahmagupta's Formula for an inscribed quadrilateral gives area $= \sqrt{(s-a)(s-b)(s-c)(s-d)}$; since s will be integral, the area is the square root of an integer. But for the area to be rational also, it must actually be integral!

C2. This is done by induction. We will just indicate the basic approach here: Given the $\overline{P}n\ ABCD\ldots TUV$, on diameter $\overline{AV}$, let the area of triangle ABC be K, the area of $ACD\ldots TV$ be K', and the area of TUV be K''. We assume that the area of any $\overline{P}(n-1)$ and any $\overline{P}(n-2)$ are integral (this is our "extended" induction assumption). Then $K + K'$ is integral, and K' is integral, so K must be integral. Since $K' + K''$ must also be integral, $K + K' + K''$ is integral.

Team Questions

T1.   If the odd integers are $n-2$, n, and $n+2$, and the 4-digit number is AAAA, we have $3n^2 + 8 = 1111\cdot A$. Since n is odd, so is A. Now either try values for A, or note that, mod 3, we have $2 \equiv A$; the only such odd digit is 5, so the answer is 5555.

T2.   The cube must be a multiple of $7^3 (= 343)$. Acceptable cubes are $1^3 \cdot 343$, $2^3 \cdot 343$, $3^3 \cdot 343, \ldots$. Therefore find $500000/343 = 1457^+$ and get the greatest cube less than that. Since $11^3 = 1331$ and $12^3 = 1728$, the answer is 11.

T3.   Let $pq = n^2 - 1$. Note that $n = 2$ doesn't work, so $pq = (n+1)(n-1)$ implies that p and q must be twin primes. But the number between twin primes is always a multiple of 6 [except for the twin primes 3 and 5] — see the end of this solution for a proof of this. Their sum is therefore of the form $12k$, so must be divisible by 12. Actually, the original problem need only have required that $p > 5$. The fact that 12 is maximum here is confirmed by noting that $101 + 103 = 12 \cdot 17$, while $107 + 109 = 12 \cdot 18$.

PROOF REFERRED TO ABOVE: Any integer must take one of the forms $6k - 1$, $6k$, $6k + 1$, $6k + 2$, $6k + 3$, or $6k + 4$. But only $6k - 1$

and $6k + 1$ could represent primes (for k greater than 0). Thus twin primes must take these forms, and the number between is a multiple of 6.

T4.   Let $AE = r$. Then $r : (5 - r) = 7 : 3$, so $r = 3^1/_2$. Now in triangle ABE, $x : y = 7 : r = 2 : 1$ or 2. Another approach would be to use "mass points", which quickly shows that

$$x : y = (a + c): b = 2 : 1.$$

T5.   We have $(3/6)+(3/6)(2/6)+(3/6)(4/6)(1/6)= 13/18$.

T6.   Represent the numbers in the circles by A (top circle); B, C, D (second line, from left to right); and E, F, G (bottom line, from left to right). Note that their sum is 28. If the "magic sum" is S, then $(A + B + E)+(A + C + F)+(A + D + G)= 3S$, so $2A + 28 = 3S$. Also, $(B + C + D)+(E + F + G)= 2S$, so $28 - A = 2S$. These two equations imply that $A = 4$, so E cannot be a 4. [Any other number is possible for E, since we can interchange any two of the "vertical" lines, or interchange the horizontal lines.]

T7.   Let the tangents from (r, s) to the curve meet the curve at (a, a^2) and (b, b^2), the first of these being above the angle bisector. Using the formula for the tangent of the angle between two lines, we have $\frac{2a-1}{1+2a} = \frac{1-2b}{1+2b}$, so $ab = \frac{1}{4}$. But the tangent lines, $y - a^2 = 2a(x - a)$ and $y - b^2 = 2b(x - b)$, intersect [solving each for x] where $\frac{y-a^2}{2a} + a = \frac{y-b^2}{2b} + b$. This produces $y[= s]= ab = \frac{1}{4}$ or 0.25.

T8.   Let t represent the length of the tangent segment, and note that $(0, 0)$, $(3, 4)$, and $(6, 8)$ all line up, forming a secant to the circle. Then $t^2 = 5 \cdot 10$, so $t = \sqrt{50}$ or $5\sqrt{2}$. The point $(5, 13)$ is totally unnecessary!

T9.   Draw perpendiculars from G to $\overline{AC}$ (meeting it at H) and $\overline{BF}$ (meeting it at J). Since $\overline{AG}$ will be a side of an inscribed regular hexagon, it has the same length as the radius; thus $AG = 7$ and angle $OAG = 60°$. Then $GH = 7\sqrt{3}/2$ and $AH = 7/2$ [making $HO = 7/2$ and, since $OB = 1$, $HB = 9/2 = GJ$]. Also, BF will be the mean proportional between AB and BC [this comes from right triangle AFC], so $BF = 4\sqrt{3}$. Now $FJ = BF - HG = \sqrt{3}/2$. We now have the legs of right triangle FGJ, leading to $k = 21$. The main purpose of this problem was to test students' understanding of certain geometric constructions.

T10. In the accompanying diagram, E and F are the centers of the circles and M and N are the midpoints of $\overline{AB}$ and $\overline{CD}$, respectively. Let $AE = EP = a$, $FP = b$, $AB = t$, $CL = LP = EK = d$, $PJ = JD = e$, and $PK = x$. Then $FG = b - a$ and $AB = t = EG = \sqrt{(b + a)^2 - (b - a)^2} = 2\sqrt{ab}$. We will use NH and MH to find MN.

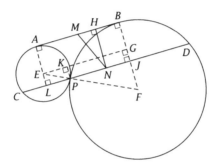

1. $x/(b - a) = a/(b + a)$ implies $x = a(b - a)/(b + a)$, so $NH = x + a = 2ab/(b + a)$.

2. $NJ = ND - JD = \frac{1}{2}(2d + 2e) - e = d$ implies $MH = MB - HB = \frac{1}{2}t - NJ = \frac{1}{2}t - d$.

3. $d/t = a/(b + a)$ implies $d = ta/(b + a)$ implies $MH = t(b - a)/2(b + a) = \frac{\sqrt{ab}(b-a)}{b+a}$.

4. $(MN)^2 = \frac{4a^2b^2}{(b+a)^2} + \frac{ab(b-a)^2}{(b+a)^2} = \frac{ab[b^2+2ab+a^2]}{(b+a)^2} = ab$ implies $MN = \sqrt{ab}[= t/2\,!] = 6$.

There are many alternate proofs yielding unexpected dividends!

Individual Questions

I1.   We are seeking four consecutive positive integers whose product is $379^2 - 1 = (379 + 1)(379 - 1) = 380 \cdot 378 = 19 \cdot 20 \cdot 378$. Since $378 = 18 \cdot 21$, $x = 18$. Incidentally, it can be easily shown that one more than the product of *any* four consecutive integers must be a perfect square!

I2. The sum of angles CDE, DCE, BAG, and ABG is $\frac{1}{2}(360°)= 180°$, so angles E and G must be supplementary. Thus quadrilateral $EFGH$ is cyclic. Let $\angle BAG = a$, $\angle ABG = b$, and $\angle BCF = c$. Then $a + b = 180 - G$ and $b + c = 180 - F$. Therefore $a - c = F - G = F - (180 - E)= E + F - 180$, so $A - C = 2[E + F - 180]= 26$ or $26°$. In general, $A - C = 2(E + F) - 360$, and $B - D = 2(E - F)$.

I3. The sum of the coefficients of $P(x)$ will be $P(1)$. Letting $x = 1$ produces $90 = 5 \cdot P(1)$, so $P(1)= 18$.

I4. Let the rectangle be $ABCD$, the center of the circle be O, the radius r, and acute angle AOD be θ. Area of $ABCD = \left(\frac{1}{2}r^2 \sin\theta\right) \cdot 4$ $= \frac{1}{2}\pi r^2$, so $\sin\theta = \frac{\pi}{4}$ which is about 0.7854. Thus θ is greater than 45° but less than (or equal to) 53° [from the angles of a 3-4-5 triangle]. Choose 49° as the wisest answer, since that will cover any integral angle from 45° through 53°! The actual angle is a bit less than 52°, so we will accept any integer angle from 48° through 56°, inclusive. For those not familiar with the angles of a 3-4-5 triangle, it is still clear that the answer is between 45° and 60°. Choosing the mean of these produces 52° or 53°, both of which are acceptable. Since the sine curve flattens out above 45°, an angle closer to 60° is the wiser choice in this case.

I5. Since the number of terms in successive rows is $1, 2, 3, 4, \ldots$, then $\frac{n(n+1)}{2} \leq 212$. This implies that $n = 20$, so we are adding the terms of the first 20 rows [that actually accounts for $\frac{20 \cdot 21}{2} = 210$ terms], plus the next two terms [which are the first two terms of row 21—namely $1 + 20$]. The sum of successive rows is $1 + 2 + 4 + 8 + \cdots + 2^{19} = 2^{20} - 1$, so the final sum is $2^{20} - 1 + 21 = 2^{20} + 20$, and $k = 20$.

I6. Note that for integer $k > 0$, $k \cdot \left[\frac{x}{k}\right]$ is the greatest multiple of k that does not exceed x. Now for integer x, $[x] - 19 \cdot \left[\frac{x}{19}\right]$ is the difference between x and the greatest multiple of 19 that does not exceed x. Therefore, x is 9 more than a multiple of 19. Also, x is 9 more than a multiple of 89. Therefore x must be 9 more than a multiple of $19 \cdot 89$. The smallest such positive x is $(19)(89)+9 = 1700$.

I7.   Each integer from 0 through $2^n - 1$ can be formed by considering n spaces, each being filled with either a 0 or a 1. There are 2^n such arrays, each of n digits, thus requiring $n \cdot 2^n$ digits. Since half those digits are 1's, we need $n \cdot 2^{n-1}$ ones. The answer is $10 \cdot 2^9 = 5120$. It is harder to count the number of 0's needed, since initial zeros cannot be counted!

I8.   Changing the order of the sides of the hexagon, in the same circle, would preserve the individual arc lengths, so the "new" hexagon would still be cyclic. (By the way, since the segment areas would also be preserved, the area of the new hexagon would be the same as that of the original!) Arranging the sides in the order $2, 7, 11, 2, 7, 11$ shows that each triplet must fit in a semicircle. Applying Ptolemy's Theorem to the quadrilateral (in a semicircle) of sides $2, 7, 11, D$ (for diameter), we have

$$\sqrt{D^2 - 121}\sqrt{D^2 - 4} = 7D + 22.$$

This implies $D^3 - 174D - 308 = 0$, or $D^3 - (2 \cdot 3 \cdot 29)D - (4 \cdot 7 \cdot 11) = 0$. We note that $11 < D < 20$; also, if D is not irrational, it is integral. Hoping to find an integral D, we see that D would be divisible by 2 but not by 3 or by 4 (else 8 would divide the constant). The only possible integer D is then 14, which works.

Relay Question #1

R1-1. From $6\sqrt{n} - 9 = n$, we find $n^2 - 18n + 81 = 0$, so $n = 9$. Student reaction to this problem was almost universal! Bewilderment, followed by frustration, anxiety, flash of insight, easy solution, satisfaction, then a smile of conquest and delight.

R1-2. We have $T = 9$ and $k = 5$. If the side of the cube is s, then $3s^2 = (k\sqrt{3})^2$, which implies $s = k$. Then volume $= k^3 = 125$.

R1-3. We have $T = 125$ and $k = 2$. From $3 | (kx^3 + 22)$, we get $3 | (kx^3 + 1)$, which implies $3 | (2x^3 + 1)$. Trial quickly produces $x = 4$.

Relay Question #2

R2-1. The middle factor must be 19. Then $(19 - x)(19)(19 + x) = 19(19^2 - x^2) > 1989$, which implies $361 - x^2 > 104.6$, so $361 - x^2 \geq 105$, $x^2 \leq 256$, and $x \leq 16$. Since the largest possible x produces the smallest next year, we use $x = 16$, getting the year $3 \cdot 19 \cdot 35 = 1995$. Without the "given that ..." in the problem, there seems to be no way to do this that does *not* involve much trial and error computation!

R2-2. We have $T = 1995$ and $n = 2$. Taking the log of each side, base 19, produces $(\log_{19} 89)(\log_{19} x) = n \cdot \log_{19} 89$, so $\log_{19} x = n$. This implies $x = 19^n = 361$.

R2-3. We have $k = 361$. Let r be the radius of the large semicircle. The area of the small semicircles $= \frac{\pi \left(\frac{r}{n} \right)^2}{2} \cdot n = \frac{\pi r^2}{2n}$. Therefore shaded area $= \frac{\pi r^2}{2} - \frac{\pi r^2}{2n} = \frac{\pi r^2 (n-1)}{2n} = k \cdot \left(\frac{\pi r^2}{2n} \right)$, which implies $n = k + 1 = 362$.

1990
American Regions
Mathematics League
Solutions

Power Question

I. A. Since $(2a)^3+(a)^3= 9a^3$, let $a = 2k^2$ and $b = k^2$. Then $(2k^2)^3+(k^2)^3= 9k^6 = (3k^3)^2$.

B. Letting $c = d/r$ and $e = dr$, we get $a^3 + b^3 = d^3$, which has no solutions.

C. We have $a^3 + b^3 = [a + b][(a + b)^2-3ab]$. Let $3ab = k^2$. Then $a^3 + b^3 = [(a + b)-k][a + b][(a + b)+k]$. Note: Choosing $b = 3$ and $a = m^2$ for example, the smallest factor will be $m^2 + 3 - 3m$, which is required to be positive. Therefore $m^2 + 3 - 3m \geq 1$, so $m^2 - 3m + 2 \geq 0$, which is easily satisfied (e.g. $m = 2$ produces $a = 4, b = 3, k = 6$).

D. We have $a^3 + b^3 = [a + b][(a + b)^2-3ab]= 3p$. Then 3 must divide one of the factors in brackets. But note that it will then also divide the other factor. Therefore 9 divides the product, so $3p$ is a multiple of 9. Thus there are no solutions for p a prime greater than 3. [Note that for $a = 2$ and $b = 1, p = 3$.]

II. A. If there are solutions, then clearly a and b have the same parity (either both are even or both are odd). If both are even, their cubes are divisible by 8; dividing through by 8 as many times as possible, we eventually reach the equation $m^3 + n^3 = 2^d$, where m and n are odd. Thus we need only consider the equation $a^3 + b^3 = 2^c$ where a and b are both odd (and $a > b$). Now $a^3 + b^3 = (a + b)(a^2 - ab + b^2) = 2^c$, which implies that each factor is a power of 2. Since $a^2 - ab + b^2$ is the sum of three odd numbers, it is odd; but the only power of 2 that is odd is $2^0 = 1$. But $a > b$ implies that $a^2 - ab + b^2 = (a - b)^2 + ab > 1$. Therefore there are no solutions.

B. Let $a = 2 \cdot 3^m$ and $b = 3^m$. Then $(2 \cdot 3^m)^3 + (3^m)^3 = 9 \cdot 3^{3m} = 3^{3m+2} = 3^c$.

C. If p divides a or b, it will divide the other also. This leads to the equation $k^3 p^3 + m^3 p^3 = p^c$, which implies that $k^3 + m^3 = p^d$. This reasoning can be repeated until neither term on the left is divisible by p. Therefore we need only consider $a^3 + b^3 = p^c$, where p does not divide a or b.

Now $a^3 + b^3 = [a + b][(a + b)^2 - 3ab] = p^c$. Noting that the second factor in brackets is greater than 1 [since it is equal to $(a - b)^2 + ab$], we see that each bracketed factor must be a power of p greater than 1. But $p|(a + b)$ and $p|(a + b)^2 - 3ab$, which implies that $p|3ab$, so $p|ab$ and thus p divides either a or b. Contradiction. Hence there are no solutions. [Note that allowing $p = 3$ destroys the validity of the ending. Also note that this proof is basically equivalent to the proof of IIA, but is more general.]

III. A. Let p be the largest prime less than c. From $p|a$ and $p|c!$, we get $p|b^3$, which implies $p|b$. Thus $p^3|a^3$ and $p^3|b^3$. Then $p^3|c!$, so $c \ge 2p$ (actually, $c \ge 3p$). But by Bertrand's Postulate (now a theorem), there is always a prime between n and $2n$ (for $n \ge 2$). Therefore there is a prime between p and $2p$, and it is less than c. Contradiction. Therefore $p \nmid a$.

B. In this solution, we will sacrifice a uniform approach to illustrate several different methods. We will show that $a + b$ is divisible by 2, 3, 5, and 11, thus establishing divisibility by 330; note that these primes divide $c!$, so they divide $a^3 + b^3$.

1. Since $a^3 + b^3$ is even, a and b must have the same parity. Then $a + b$ is even, so $2|(a + b)$.

2. We have $a^3 + b^3 = [a + b][(a + b)^2 - 3ab]$. Either 3 divides the first factor, or it divides the second factor

[in which case it must divide $(a + b)^2$ and therefore $a + b$]. Thus $3 | (a + b)$.

3. If $5 | a$, it must divide b, so $5 | (a + b)$. Suppose 5 does not divide a or b. Fermat's Little Theorem states that if p is a prime and $\gcd(a, p) = 1$, then $a^{p-1} \equiv 1$ (mod p). Thus, for example, $a^4 \equiv b^4 \equiv 1$ (mod 5). Now $a^3 + b^3 \equiv 0$ (mod 5). Multiplying by ab, we find $a^4 b + ab^4 \equiv 0$, which implies that $b + a \equiv 0$, so $5 | (a + b)$. This approach can be applied for each prime under consideration here, although (mod 11) requires additional clever manipulation.

4. Consider a number of the form $11k + x$, and let its cube be of the form $11K + y$, $0 \le x, y < 11$. A table comparing x and y is as follows:

x	0	1	2	3	4	5	6	7	8	9	10
y	0	1	8	5	9	4	7	2	6	3	10

Note how when two y values add up to 11 (or 0), the corresponding x values add up to 11 (or 0). Thus since $11 | (a^3 + b^3)$, $11 | (a + b)$. This approach can be applied for each prime under consideration. [It also works for products of some of these primes, such as 6 and 10. It will work to show that $17 | (a + b)$, if c is large enough. Try it for divisibility by 7 to see how it fails.]

The question of whether $a^3 + b^3 = c!$ has solutions for $c > 2$ may be an open question.

Team Questions

T1.   For the greatest sum, we place the largest digits in the tens positions, getting $10(9 + 8 + 7 + 6 + 5) + (4 + 3 + 2 + 1 + 0) = 360$. The greatest odd sum is gotten by interchanging the positions of the 5 and 4, getting 351. Thus the answer is 9 or -9 [either one is acceptable]. Try showing that the sum can never be a prime!

T2.   The segments joining vertices can only be edges, face diagonals, or diagonals that go through the center of the cube. Since

AB, AC, and BC are all different, the longest, AC, has the center of the cube as its midpoint. Hence the answer is $(3, 2, 4)$.

T3. We have

$$
\begin{array}{r}
.0\quad\ldots\text{A67}\,|\,\ldots \\
\hline
97\,|\,1.000\ldots000\,|\,00\ldots
\end{array}
$$

Since the repetend begins again after the vertical line, the remainder just after that vertical is a 1. Thus $97(0\ldots\text{A67}) + 1 = 1000\ldots000$. Doing the multiplication:

```
0  ...  A  6  7
            9  7
```
```
   ...  *  6  9      * in this position, we put the units digit of
   ...  0  3             (7A + 4)
        +  1
   ...  0  0  0
```

Thus $(7A + 4)+1$ ends in a 0, so $7A$ ends in a 5, and A must be 5.

T4. The soldier's effective rate running toward the front (as if the others were standing still) is $(4 - 2) = 2$ mph; running toward the back it is $(4 + 2) = 6$ mph. The total time $[= \frac{\text{dist}}{\text{rate}}]$ he has run is $\frac{1/8}{2} + \frac{1/8}{6} = 1/12$. Therefore the total distance $[= \text{rate}\cdot\text{time}]$ he has run is $(4)(1/12) = 1/3$ mile.

T5. If the dimensions of the cardboard are x and y, we have

$$(1)\,(x - 2)(y - 2) = (2)(x - 4)(y - 4)$$

which implies that $xy - 6x - 6y = -28$. The volume we want is

$$(3)(x - 6)(y - 6) = (3xy - 18x - 18y)+108$$
$$= 3(-28)+108 = 24.$$

T6. Any set of six different digits produces one such number. Since we cannot include a 0 (six digits beginning with 0 constitute at best what is commonly known as a 5-digit number), the answer is $\binom{9}{6} = 84$.

T7. We see that $a + b + ab = n$ is equivalent to $(a + 1)(b + 1)= n+1$. Since each factor on the left is at least 2, $n + 1$ cannot be prime.

Thus the values of n that do NOT work are those numbers that are one less than a prime. In this case $n = 96$ and 100 [both required].

T8.   Draw $\overline{AE} \| \overline{BC}$, and $\overline{BF}$ and $\overline{CG}$ each perpendicular to $\overline{AE}$. Then $BF = 2\sqrt{3} = CG$, so $CE = 4$ making $ED = 1$. Also, $AF = 2\sqrt{3}$ and $GE = 2$, so $AE = 9$. Applying the Law of Cosines to triangle $AED (\sphericalangle AED = 120°)$ produces $AD = \sqrt{91}$.

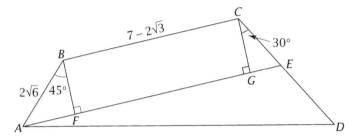

For a simpler (but less unusual) solution by coordinate geometry, place B at the origin and C on the positive x-axis. Get the coordinates of A and D, and apply the distance formula.

T9.   If the term immediately following 305 is x, we have $\dots, 305, x,$ $305 + x, 305 + 2x, 610 + 3x, 915 + 5x, 1525 + 8x, \dots$. Since one of these must be 1990, and x must be an integer greater than 305, we find that either $x = 1685$ or $x = 460$. The smallest first term will occur if we use $x = 460$. Working backwards produces the terms (before 305) 155, 150, and 5.

T10. *Method 1*: [Note: If $\tan A$ and $\tan B$ are defined, $\tan A = -\tan B$ implies $\sin A / \cos A = -\sin B / \cos B$. Thus

$$\sin A \cos B + \cos A \sin B = 0$$

and we have $\sin(A + B) = 0$, so $A + B$ is an integer multiple of 180°.]

Using "sums into products" formulas,

$$\tan(120 - x) = \frac{2 \cos \frac{120+x}{2} \sin \frac{120-x}{2}}{-2 \sin \frac{120+x}{2} \sin \frac{120-x}{2}}$$

$$= -\cot \frac{120 + x}{2}$$

$$= -\tan[90 - (\frac{120 + x}{2})]$$

$$= -\tan \frac{60 - x}{2}.$$

Then $(120 - x) + (\frac{60-x}{2}) = \frac{300-3x}{2} = 180k$, k an integer. Since $0 < x < 180$, we have $150 > \frac{300-3x}{2} > -120$, so $\frac{300-3x}{2} = 0$, which implies $x = 100$ [or $100°$]. Note that $x = 30°$ or $120°$, values of x not permissible in the original equation, would not satisfy that equation even in the "limiting" case.

Method 2: Expressing $\tan(120° - x)$ as $\frac{\sin(120°-x)}{\cos(120°-x)}$, expanding numerator and denominator, and cross-multiplying with the right side of the original equation, we get

$$(\sin 120° \cos x - \sin x \cos 120°)(\cos 120° - \cos x)$$

$$= (\cos 120° \cos x + \sin 120° \sin x)(\sin 120° - \sin x).$$

Putting in the values for $\sin 120°$ and $\cos 120°$, multiplying out and simplifying the result, we eventually get $-4 \sin x = 2 \sin 2x + 2\sqrt{3} \cos 2x$. Dividing through by 4 now leads to $\sin (-x) = \sin(60° + 2x)$. Considering the possible cases, only $x = 100$ satisfies the given conditions.

Individual Questions

I1.   More generally (and more easily),

$$\frac{(a + b)^3 - a^3 - b^3}{(a + b)(a)(b)} = \frac{3a^2b + 3ab^2}{(a + b)(a)(b)} = \frac{3ab(a + b)}{(a + b)(a)(b)} = 3.$$

I2.   From $|(2C + 30) - (\frac{9}{5}C + 32)| \le 1$, we get $-1 \le \frac{C}{5} - 2 \le 1$, which implies that $5 \le C \le 15$. Thus, the answer is $(5, 15)$.

I3.   Adding the first and third equations, $a + b + c + d = a + c$, which implies that $b + d = 0$ and thus $d = -b$. This leads to $c = -2b$ and $a = -3b$, so $a + b + c + d = -5b$. The maximum sum occurs for $b = 1$, producing -5. [Note: $(a, b, c, d) = (-3, 1, -2, -1)$.]

I4.   The test for divisibility by 3 shows that $3A + 3B + C$ must not be a multiple of 3; therefore $C \ne 0, 3$, or 9. Also, for the number to be prime, $C \neq 2, 4, 5, 6$, or 8. Therefore $C = 1$ or 7. The test for divisibility by 11 shows that

$$(2A + B + C) - (2B + A) = (A - B) + C = 4 + C$$

must not be a multiple of 11. Therefore $C \neq 7$, so $C = 1$. Since $A - B = 4$ and A is prime, we can only have $(A, B) = (5, 1)$ or $(7,3)$. Since $C = 1$, the answer must be $(A, B, C) = (7, 3, 1)$. Note that this analysis shows that no number other than 7,773,331 can fit all the requirements. It does not prove that this number actually *is* a prime, as the problem hypothesizes! A check by computer has confirmed the primality. (This leads to the interesting question of how we created the problem.)

I5.   We have

$$2 = \log(k!)^2 - \log(k - 2)! - \log(k - 1)! = \log[k!k!/(k - 2)!(k - 1)!]$$

which implies that $\log 100 = \log k^2(k - 1)$, so $k^2(k - 1) = 100 = 5 \cdot 5 \cdot 4$ and hence $k = 5$.

I6.   Clearly $f(x)$ cannot exceed 2. We get 2 if $x/3$ and $x/11$ each have a reference angle of $90°$. Setting $x/3 = 90 + 360a$ and $x/11 = 90 + 360b$ leads to $x = 3(90 + 360a) = 11(90 + 360b)$, which implies that $3a - 11b = 2$. The smallest nonnegative solution to this is $b = 2, a = 8$, whereupon $x = 8910$ (or $8910°$). A solution using calculus is just a little harder!

I7.   From $x^2 - x + y^2 - y = 0$ we get $(x - 1/2)^2 + (y - 1/2)^2 = 1/2$. For maximum x, let $(y - 1/2)^2 = 0$, so $x - 1/2 = 1/\sqrt{2}$ and $x = (1 + \sqrt{2})/2$ or equivalent. This generalizes beautifully to

$$x_1^2 + x_2^2 + \cdots + x_n^2 = x_1 + x_2 + \cdots + x_n,$$

leading to maximum $x_1 = (1 + \sqrt{n})/2$.

The equation can also be thought of as representing a sphere in n dimensions, center at $(1/2, 1/2, \ldots)$, radius $\sqrt{n}/2$; for $n = 2$, an analytic geometry solution shows the rightmost point of the circle to be at $(1/2 + \sqrt{2}/2, 1/2)$.

I8.   Let the sides be $4n - 1$, $4n$, and $4n + 1$, so the semiperimeter (s) is $6n$. Hero's formula for area gives

$$A = \sqrt{(6n)(2n + 1)(2n)(2n - 1)} = 2n\sqrt{3(2n + 1)(2n - 1)},$$

so we must have $(2n + 1)(2n - 1) = 3k^2$. The factors on the left are both odd so they can have no common factors (since they differ by 2). Thus one must be an odd square (but not a multiple of 3), while the other is 3 times an odd square. We make a short table:

odd square (not a multiple of 3)	odd square ±2 (= 3 times a square)
1	3 [= 3 · 1]
25	27 [= 3 · 9]

In the first case we have $2n - 1 = 1$, so $n = 1$ and $4n = 4$ giving a 3-4-5 triangle. In the second case we have $2n - 1 = 25$, so $n = 13$ and $4n = 52$, and the answer is 51, 52, 53. Note that $A = 1170$. Solving generally for such triangles leads to the equation $N^2 - 1 = 3k^2$ [a form of Pell's equation], where N is half the middle side (which *must* always be even). The case $N = 2$ produces the 3-4-5 triangle; $N = 7$ produces the 13-14-15 triangle; etc.

Relay #1

R1-1. The third side must be 61. The altitude to the base will be 60, so the area is 660.

R1-2. We have $T = 660$ and $K = 661$. Simplifying $[a + (b + c)/2]/2 - [(a + b)/2 + c]/2$ produces $(a - c)/4$. The greatest value for this would be $(K - 1)/4$, which equals 165.

R1-3. We have $T = 165$. Since $[n/2] \le n/2$ and $[n/3] \le n/3$, equality occurs if and only if each fraction is an integer. Therefore n is an integer multiple of 6. For $1 \le n \le T$, the answer would be $[T/6]$; for the strict inequality, the answer is $[(T - 1)/6] = [164/6] = 27$.

Relay #2

R2-1. If the dimensions of the box are a, b, and c, then $ab + ac = 25$, which implies that $a(b + c) = 25$ so $a = 5$ and $b + c = 5$. Thus b and c are 2 and 3, so $bc = 6$.

R2-2. We have $T = 6$ and $K = 67$. Trying some examples, we find that 1, 2, or 3 digits uses 0 commas; 4, 5, or 6 digits uses 1 comma; etc. Thus n digits uses $[(n - 1)/3]$ commas. Our number uses $[\frac{(K+5)-1}{3}] = [\frac{K+4}{3}] = [71/3] = 23$ commas.

R2-3. We have $k = 23$. Clearly the three small triangles are equilateral, with the two smallest being congruent. If $PS = x$, then $PA = SB = (20-x)/2 = PQ = SR$, and $QR = CQ = 20-[(20-x)/2] = (20 + x)/2$. Thus $k = (60 - x)/2 = 23$, so $x = 14$.

1991
American Regions
Mathematics League
Solutions

Power Question

I.   1a.   We see that $\sin(180° - A) = \sin A$ [rational]; $\cos(180° - A) = -\cos A$ [rational]; thus supplement of A is "nice."

1b.   We see that $90°$ is nice, but $45°$ is not nice; however, $\sin 2A = 2\sin A\cos A$ [rational] and $\cos 2A = \cos^2 A - \sin^2 A$ [rational]. Thus $\frac{1}{2}A$ need not be nice, but $2A$ will be nice.

1c.   Let A and B be nice. Expanding $\sin(A+B)$ and $\cos(A+B)$ shows that $A + B$ will be nice. Thus the set of nice angles is closed under addition. [We can show closure under subtraction also, of course.] These closure facts actually prove parts (1a) and [part of] (1b) above.

2a.   Let acute angle A be nice, with $\sin A = p/q$ and $\cos A = r/s$ [all letters represent positive integers]. Then $\sin A = ps/qs$ and $\cos A = qr/qs$; since $\sin^2 A + \cos^2 A = 1$, $(ps)^2 + (qr)^2 = (qs)^2$. Thus angle A is an angle of a Pythagorean triangle with sides ps, qr, and [hypotenuse] qs.

2b.   By (2a) above, angle A must be an angle of a Pythagorean triangle, and therefore an angle of a "primitive" Pythagorean triangle [no integer greater than 1 divides all three sides]. It is well known that such a triangle has one even leg, one odd leg, and an odd hypotenuse. Thus cos A must be equivalent to a fraction with an odd denominator [and this, when reduced, could never become a fraction with an even denominator].

2c.   Any positive odd integer larger than 1 can be the leg of a Pythagorean triangle, and the other two sides can be consecutive integers [e.g. starting with 7,

$$7^2 = 49 = 25 + 24 = (25 + 24)(25 - 24) = 25^2 - 24^2;$$

the sides of the triangle would be 7,24,25]. If the leg opposite angle A is k [odd], then the other sides can be $(k^2 - 1)/2$ and $(k^2 + 1)/2$. Now cos $A = (k^2 - 1)/(k^2 + 1)$, and as k gets larger and larger, cos A approaches 1. Thus A approaches $0°$.

II.   1.   Consider triangle ABC, with rational sides, and with "nice" angle A. We will show that angle B must be nice. The Law of Sines shows that sin $B = (b/a)(\sin A)$ [rational]; the Law of Cosines shows that cos $B = (a^2 + c^2 - b^2)/2ac$ [rational]. Thus angle B is nice.

2a.   If we join two 3-4-5 triangles along their 4 unit sides, with their 3 unit sides lining up to form one long base, we can create a 5-5-6 triangle. Since each angle of a 3-4-5 triangle is nice, the vertex angle of this isosceles triangle is nice [by I(1c) above], and its base angles are nice. Also, since the smaller acute angle of a 3-4-5 triangle is less than $45°$, our new vertex angle is acute (as are the other angles of this isosceles triangle). The perimeter is 16. [It can be shown that *no* integer-sided nice triangle has a smaller perimeter except the 3-4-5 triangle.]

2b.   If the sides of our nice triangle are all even, then its area will be an even multiple of the area of a smaller (similar) nice triangle whose sides are not all even. We will prove that this smaller triangle also has an even (integer) area. Thus, assume that our triangle does *not* have 3 even sides. Every triangle must have an acute angle. In our problem, let that be (nice) angle A. Then cos $A = (b^2 + c^2 - a^2)/2bc$.

When this is reduced, the denominator must become odd [by I(2b) above]; therefore the original numerator must be even. That can only happen if (either 0 or) 2 of the sides are odd; but that means the perimeter of the triangle will be even! Applying Hero's formula for area (and noting that the semiperimeter is therefore an integer), we see that the area will be the square root of an integer. We next note that Area $= \frac{1}{2}bc \sin A$ implies that the area is rational. For the square root of an integer to be rational, that integer must be a perfect square. Thus the area itself is an integer. Finally, we look again at the radicand in Hero's formula. If s is even, then the radicand is even; if s is odd, then (since two of the sides are odd) some of the other factors will be even, so the radicand is even. In either case, the square root of an even integer that is a perfect square must also be even, so the area of our triangle is an *even* integer.

III.   Let the quadrilateral be $ABCD$; we will prove that angle A (chosen arbitrarily) is nice. Let $AB = a, BC = b, CD = c, DA = d$, and $BD = e$. Since $ABCD$ is cyclic, angles A and C are supplementary, so $\cos C = -\cos A$. Now

$$\cos A = \frac{a^2 + d^2 - e^2}{2ad} = \frac{a^2 + d^2 - [b^2 + c^2 - 2bc(-\cos A)]}{2ad}.$$

Clearing fractions and solving for $\cos A$, we get

$$\cos A = \frac{(a^2 + d^2) - (b^2 + c^2)}{2(ad + bc)},$$

which is rational (since the sides are integers).

Since this quadrilateral can be circumscribed about a circle, it must be true that $a + c = b + d$ (!). [This well-known fact can be proved by considering the lengths of tangent segments to the circle from each vertex of $ABCD$.] Thus, its semiperimeter s is equal to $a + c$ (or $b + d$). Now Brahmagupta's formula for the area of an inscribed quadrilateral is

$$\text{Area } = \sqrt{(s - a)(s - b)(s - c)(s - d)}$$

[notice that letting one side become 0, so the quadrilateral becomes a triangle, we get the more familiar formula for the area of a triangle!]; but for our quadrilateral, we can replace each s in this formula by either $a + c$ or $b + d$ (whichever is most appropriate), getting the wonderful formula for a quadrilateral that is both inscriptable and circumscriptable, Area $= \sqrt{abcd}$. Since we are given that $abcd$ is a square, our area is an integer. Finally, noting that $\sin C = \sin A$, we see that the area (K) of $ABCD$ is also given by $\frac{1}{2}(ad + bc)\sin A$, so $\sin A = 2K/(ad + bc)$; since K is an integer (from our previous work), $\sin A$ is rational. Thus angle A is nice, and our quadrilateral is nice! Incidentally, the quadrilateral of smallest perimeter with these properties has sides 1,2,9,8 (in that order). For those interested, it can be proven that the only *regular* polygon that is nice is the square.

Team Questions

T1. *Method 1*: This calls for a "double" application of the pigeonhole principle: Some jar *must* contain (at least) 13 marbles. At least five of these must be of the same color.

     Method 2: There must be (at least) 41 marbles of the same color. Some jar must contain at least five of these.

T2.   ABBA   Clearly E $= 1$, so (from the rightmost column,
    +CDDC   since neither A nor C can be 0) A $+$ C $= 11$. Then
    EFGFE   (from the leftmost column) F $= 1$ or 2 (if there is a "carry"), so the maximum F is 2. This quickly leads to C $= 2$, so N $= 12221$. [The only other possible value for N is 11111.]

T3. We have
$$\frac{\binom{n}{101}}{\binom{n}{100}} = \frac{n!100!(n-100)!}{101!(n-101)!n!} = (n-100)/101 = k > 1$$

[else $\binom{n}{101} = \binom{n}{100}$]. Using $k = 2$, we find that $n = 302$.

T4. We have
$$(x-1)(x^2+x+1)(x^6+x^3+1) = (x^3-1)(x^6+x^3+1) = x^9-1 = 10$$
which implies that $x^9 = 11$, so $x = \sqrt[9]{11}$.

T5. We will graph each side of this equation separately, then see
     how many times the graphs intersect. First graph $y = x^2 - 1$
     [parabola], then $y = |x^2 - 1|$ [the part of the first parabola that
     was below the x-axis reflects so it is now above that axis], then
     $y = |x^2 - 1| - 1$ [previous graph is translated down 1 unit], then
     $y = ||x^2 - 1| - 1|$ [graph has three minimum points on the x-
     axis, and two relative maximum points with ordinates equal to
     1]. The graph of $y = 2^x$ clearly crosses the other graph at three
     points.

T6. Draw triangle ABC, with $AB = 9$, $AC = 15$, $BC = x$, $\angle ACB = \theta$,
     and $\angle ABC = 2\theta$.

     Method 1: Extend $\overline{AB}$ through B to D so that $BD = BC = x$. The
     base angles of triangle BDC are congruent and add up to 2θ,
     so each equals θ. Thus triangles ADC and ABC are similar, so
     $(9 + x)/15 = 15/9$, which implies $x = 16$.

     Method 2: In triangle ABC, $9/\sin\theta = 15/\sin 2\theta$, so $\cos\theta = 5/6$.
     Applying the Law of Cosines, $81 = 225 + x^2 - 2(15)(x)(5/6)$,
     so $x = 9$ or 16. However $x = 9$ makes triangle ABC isosceles,
     leading to $2\theta = 90°$ (impossible, since $9^2 + 9^2 \neq 15^2$).

     Method 3: Drop an altitude (of length h) from A, cutting the
     base into segments of length p (nearer to B) and q. Then

     $$p/9 = \cos 2\theta = 2\cos^2\theta - 1 = 2(q/15)^2 - 1,$$

     so $25p = 2q^2 - 225$. Then $h^2 = 81 - p^2 = 225 - q^2$ which
     implies $q^2 = 144 + p^2$, so $25p = 288 + 2p^2 - 225$, leading to
     $p = 9$ (impossible) or $p = 7/2$; then $q = 25/2$ and $x = 16$.

T7. *Method 1*: Since the radius is 1, a 60° arc is subtended by a chord
     of length 1. Therefore we are looking for the first chord whose
     arc is less than 60°. Minor arc $P_1P_2 = 180° - 2°$; in degrees
     minor arc $P_2P_3 = 180 - (2 + 4) = 180 - 2(1 + 2)$; minor arc
     $P_3P_4 = 180 - (2 + 4 + 6) = 180 - 2(1 + 2 + 3)$; in general, minor
     arc $P_kP_{k+1} = 180 - 2(1 + 2 + 3 + \cdots + k) = 180 - 2 \cdot k(k+1)/2 < 60$,
     which implies that $k(k + 1) > 120$, so $k = 11$.

     Method 2: Redraw the semicircle only, with diameter $\overline{AB}$ of
     length 2. From B draw a chord at a 1° angle with the diame-
     ter [its length will be $2\cos 1°$; this can be seen by connecting
     the other end of the chord to A and noticing that a right triangle

is formed]; from B draw another chord at a $2°$ angle with the previous chord and above it [its length will be $2\cos(1+2)°$; this can be seen by connecting the other end of the chord to A and noticing that a right triangle is formed]; etc. The chords here have the same length as the chords in the original given diagram [compare the arcs subtended by the two sets of chords]! The chord we are seeking has the property that $2\cos(1+2+3+\cdots+k)<1$, so $\cos k(k+1)/2 < \frac{1}{2}$, whereupon $k(k+1)/2 > 60$, so $k > 10$.

T8.   Note that $x_n + iy_n = (2\operatorname{cis}60°)^n = 2^n\operatorname{cis}60°\cdot n$.

Method 1: We have $x_{19}+iy_{19} = 2^{19}\operatorname{cis}60°\cdot 19 = 2^{19}\operatorname{cis}1140° = 2^{19}\operatorname{cis}60°$, so $x_{19} = 2^{19}\cos60°$ and $y_{19} = 2^{19}\sin60°$. Thus $x_{91} + iy_{91} = 2^{91}\operatorname{cis}60°\cdot 91 = 2^{91}\operatorname{cis}5460° = 2^{91}\operatorname{cis}60°$, so $x_{91} = 2^{91}\cos60°$, and $y_{91} = 2^{91}\sin60°$. Therefore

$$x_{19}y_{91} + x_{91}y_{19} = 2[2^{110}\cos60°\sin60°] = 2^{109}\sqrt{3};$$

thus $k = 109$.

Method 2: We see that

$$(x_{19} + iy_{19})(x_{91} + iy_{91}) = x_{19}x_{91} - y_{19}y_{91} + i(x_{19}y_{91} + x_{91}y_{19})$$

$$= x_{19}x_{91} - y_{19}y_{91} + i(2^k\sqrt{3}).$$

Changing the first product to polar form and multiplying, we get

$$(2^{19}\operatorname{cis}60°\cdot 19)(2^{91}\operatorname{cis}60°\cdot 91) = 2^{110}\operatorname{cis}60°\cdot 110$$

$$= 2^{110}\operatorname{cis}6600°$$

$$= 2^{110}\operatorname{cis}120°$$

$$= 2^{110}(\cos120° + i\sin120°).$$

Equating imaginary parts of our equality produces

$$2^k\sqrt{3} = 2^{110}\sin120° = 2^{110}\cdot\sqrt{3}/2 = 2^{109}\sqrt{3},$$

so $k = 109$.

T9.   From the diagram on the next page, $\sin\theta = x/r = h/2r$, so $x = h/2$; then $PQ = 2x+m = h+m = 8+[(18+30)/2] = 32$. Try drawing semicircles outward on the *bases*, and find the distance between the midpoints of *those* arcs. Surprised?

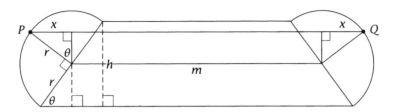

T10.   We want the smallest positive integer x for which $a^2 - p = x$ is impossible. Consider $a^2 - x = p$, and first try $x = y^2$ (because of its factorability). The equation $(a + y)(a - y) = p$ implies $a + y = p, a - y = 1$, which implies $a = y + 1$, so $2y + 1 = p$. The smallest y for which this fails is $y = 4$, so $x = 16$. To see if a smaller x can be used, we must try $a^2 - 1 = p$, $a^2 - 2 = p$, $\dots, a^2 - 15 = p$. A solution to each of these is easily found [e.g. $2^2 - 1, 5^2 - 2, 4^2 - 3, \dots, 14^2 - 15$], so the answer is 16. Has this problem a solution if the prime is greater than the square?

Individual Questions

I1.   *Method 1*: Adding all the equations produces

$$A + 2(B + C + D + \cdots + Y) + Z = 25 \cdot 26/2 = 325,$$

so $2(A + B + \cdots + Z) - A - Z = 325$. Adding every other equation produces

$$A + B + C + D + \cdots + Y + Z = 1 + 3 + 5 + \cdots + 25 = 13^2 = 169.$$

Thus $2(169) - A - Z = 325$, so $A + Z = 13$.

Method 2: Alternately adding and subtracting equations produces

$$(A + B) - (B + C) + (C + D) - \cdots - (X + Y) + (Y + Z)$$
$$= 1 - 2 + 3 - \cdots - 24 + 25,$$

so $A + Z = 13$.

Method 3: We find in succession $B = 1 - A$, $C = 2 - B = 1 + A$, $D = 3 - C = 2 - A$, $E = 2 + A, \dots$, and $Z = 13 - A$, so $A + Z = 13$.

Method 4: Since there are more variables than equations, we can assign an arbitrary value to a letter; e.g. let $A = 0$. Then $B = 1, C = 1, D = 2, E = 2, \ldots, Z = 13$, so $A + Z = 13$.

What does $A + R + M + L$ equal?

I2.   The left side becomes $\frac{(3-1)(3+1)}{3 \cdot 3} \cdot \frac{(4-1)(4+1)}{4 \cdot 4} \cdots \frac{(1991-1)(1991+1)}{1991 \cdot 1991} =$
$\frac{2 \cdot \cancel{4}}{3 \cdot \cancel{3}} \cdot \frac{\cancel{3} \cdot \cancel{5}}{\cancel{4} \cdot \cancel{4}} \cdot \frac{\cancel{4} \cdot \cancel{6}}{\cancel{3} \cdot \cancel{3}} \cdots \frac{\cancel{1989} \cdot \cancel{1991}}{\cancel{1990} \cdot \cancel{1990}} \cdot \frac{\cancel{1990} \cdot 1992}{\cancel{1991} \cdot 1991} =$ [cancelling almost all the terms in numerator and denominator] $\frac{2}{3} \cdot \frac{1992}{1991} = \frac{x}{1991}$, which implies that $x = 1328$.

I3.   Since Area $= ab/2 = 4$, we see that $ab = 8$. Thus

$$\text{Sin } 2A = 2 \sin A \cos A = 2(a/12)(b/12) = ab/72 = 8/72 = 1/9.$$

Notice that the same holds for $\sin 2B$, leading to the result that if A and B are complementary, $\sin 2A = \sin 2B$. Of course, now that seems so obvious!

I4.   Draw a circle with center $P(-5, 0)$, passing through $Q(5, 0)$, and draw the line $y = 6$. Clearly $(0, 6)$ is a point that satisfies the conditions of the problem. The circle crosses $y = 6$ at two more satisfactory points; we find their x-coordinates by solving the pair of simultaneous equations: $(x + 5)^2 + y^2 = 100, y = 6$; these lead to $x = 3, -13$. Finally, we consider a circle whose center is Q, passing through P, and see where it crosses $y = 6$; by symmetry to the previous circle, the x-coordinates of these crossing points would be $x = -3, +13$. Answers: $0, \pm 3, \pm 13$.

I5.   *Method 1*: The fraction is equal to

$$\frac{9 \cdot 3^{29} + 4 \cdot 2^{29}}{3^{29} + 2^{29}} = \frac{8(3^{29} + 2^{29}) + 3^{29} - 4 \cdot 2^{29}}{3^{29} + 2^{29}} = 8 + \frac{3^{29} - 2^{31}}{3^{29} + 2^{29}}.$$

Since that last fraction is clearly positive, but less than 1, the answer is 8.

Method 2: By long division,

$$
\begin{array}{r}
9 \\
3^{29} + 2^{29} \overline{\big)\ 3^{31} \qquad\qquad +2^{31}} \\
\underline{3^{31} + 9 \cdot 2^{29}} \\
-9 \cdot 2^{29} \quad +2^{31} \ = -5 \cdot 2^{29}
\end{array}
$$

The quotient is $9 - \frac{5 \cdot 2^{29}}{3^{29} + 2^{29}}$.

Clearly the last fraction is less than 1, so the answer is 8.

I6. Graphing the first equation [by considering $x \le 1, 1 < x < 3,$ and $x \ge 3$] and finding its intersections with $y = 8$ [$(-2, 8)$ and $(6, 8)$], we get the lengths of the trapezoid's bases [8 and 2] and its height [6]. The required area is $(1/2)(6)(8 + 2) = 30$.

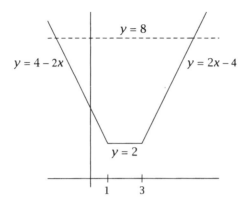

I7. Letting $AQ = x$, we have $AR = 5 - x$ and $BR = 3$. Using the Law of Cosines to get the missing side of each small triangle, then applying the Pythagorean Theorem to the sides of the right triangle, we get

$$[2^2 + 3^2 - 2 \cdot 3] + [2^2 + x^2 - 2x] = [3^2 + (5 - x)^2 - 3(5 - x)],$$

which leads to $x = 8/5$ or 1.6.

I8. Consider $N = a^k - b^k + c^k$. Since $a^k - b^k$ is divisible by $a - b$, N is divisible by the greatest common divisor (gcd) of $a - b$ and c^k. Thus N is divisible by $\gcd(85 - 21, 6^9) = \gcd(64, 6^9) = 2^6$. Similarly, N is divisible by $\gcd(21 - 6, 85^9) = 5$. Furthermore, when k is odd, $a^k + c^k$ is divisible by $a + c$; thus N is also divisible by $\gcd(85 + 6, 21^9) = 7$. Since the divisors we have found are relatively prime, N must be divisible by $2^6 \cdot 5 \cdot 7 = 2240$. In fact, $N = 231616152013234240 = 2^6 \cdot 5 \cdot 7 \cdot 79699 \cdot 1297382249$ (the final two factors are primes).

Relay #1

R1-1. If the answer is N, then

$$N = 100h + 10t + u, 7 \mid N \quad \text{and} \quad 7 \mid (h + t + u).$$

This implies $7 \mid (99h + 9t)$, so $7 \mid 9(11h + t)$, so $7 \mid (11h + t)$. Letting $h = 1$, we have $t = 3$. Then $7 \mid (1 + 3 + u)$, which implies that $u = 3$, so $N = 133$. Of course, starting at 105 and repeatedly adding 7 quickly leads to the answer.

R1-2. We have $T = 133$ and $B = 3$. Thus

$$B^{(\log 4)+(\log 25)} = B^{\log 100} = B^2 = (T - 130)^2 = 9.$$

R1-3. We have $T = 9$.

Method 1: If the legs are a and b, ab is constant (equal to $2T$), as is $a^2 b^2$. But if the product of two positive numbers (a^2 and b^2) is constant, their sum is a minimum when they are equal. Thus $a = b = \sqrt{2T}$, and the hypotenuse is $\sqrt{a^2 + b^2} = \sqrt{4T} = 2\sqrt{T} = 6$.

Method 2: The shortest hypotenuse calls for the longest altitude to that hypotenuse. Considering a semicircle on the hypotenuse, the third vertex of the triangle must lie on that semicircle. The longest altitude comes from an isosceles triangle.

Method 3: Let the hypotenuse be c. Given two positive numbers, their arithmetic mean is greater than or equal to their geometric mean. Thus $(a^2 + b^2)/2 \geq \sqrt{a^2 b^2} = ab$ which implies $c^2/2 \geq 2T$, so $c \geq 2\sqrt{T} = 6$.

Relay #2

R2-1. From $(6p)(qr) = (c/a)(a/c) = 1$, we see that $pqr = 1/6$. One can show that the roots of the second equation are the reciprocals of the roots of the first. This also shows that the product of all four roots is 1.

R2-2. We have $T = 1/6$ and $L = 6$. Let $AE = 2x = CE$. Then $BE = x = DE$, so $CD = CE - DE = x = L/3 = 12T = 2$.

R2-3. We have $Q = 2$. Let the distance from $P(a, b)$ to the center of the circle be $\sqrt{k}$, where $k > 31$. Since P is a lattice point, k is an integer. Trying $k = 32$, we have $(a - 1)^2 + (b - 2)^2 = 32$. The only possible solutions to this come from $a - 1 = \pm 4$, $b - 2 = \pm 4$. These correspond to the points $(5, 6), (-3, 6), (-3, -2)$, and $(5, -2)$. In quadrant II, the closest point is $(-3, 6)$.

1992 American Regions Mathematics League Solutions

Power Question

I. [The area formula can be gotten by using determinants or by enclosing the triangle in a rectangle.] (1) Since at least two of the abscissas must have the same parity, their difference is divisible by 2. (2) Suppose that $a < b < c, K = p$ [prime], $b - a = e$, $c - b = f$, and $c - a = e + f$. Then $2p = ef(e + f)$. At least one factor must be a 1, say $e = 1$. Then $f(f + 1) = 2p$. If $f = 1$, $2 = 2p$ [impossible]; therefore $f = 2$ and $p = 3$ only. (3) Let $ef(e + f) = 2p^2$. If $e = 1$, $f(f + 1) = 2p^2$; either $f = 1$, so $2 = 2p^2$ [impossible] OR $f = 2$, so $6 = 2p^2$ [impossible] OR $f = p$, so $f + 1 = 2p$ [implies $p + 1 = 2p$; impossible]. If $e = 2$, $f(2 + f) = p^2$ [both $f = 1$ and $f = p$ lead to impossibilities]. (4) A diagonal must cut the quadrilateral into two triangles, each with integer area. But any pair of positive integers whose sum is 8 has at least one integer that is a square or a prime not equal to 3 [impossible].

II. [Slope $= (a^2 - b^2)/(a - b) = a + b$.] (1) Let the two points be (a, a^2) and (b, b^2). Then $(5 - a^2)/(3 - a) = a + b$ leads to

$$b = (5 - 3a)/(3 - a) = 3 + 4/(a - 3).$$

Trying $a - 3 = \pm 1, \pm 2, \pm 4$ leads to only two pairs of values for a and b [order not important] with $a \neq b$, namely $a = -1, b = 2$, and $a = 4, b = 7$. The pairs of points are $(-1, 1), (2, 4)$ and $(4, 16), (7, 49)$.

(2) Let the points be $(a, -a^2)$ and $(b, -b^2)$ on the "lower" parabola $[y = -x^2]$ and (c, c^2) on the "upper" parabola. Then

$$(4 + b^2)/(2 - b) = (4 + a^2)/(2 - a) = 2 + c.$$

The first equality leads eventually to $b = (2a + 4)/(a - 2) = 2 + 8/(a - 2)$. Trying $a - 2 = \pm 1, \pm 2, \pm 4, \pm 8$ leads to only four pairs of values for a and b [order not important] with $a \neq b$, namely $a = 3, b = 10$ and $a = -6, b = 1$ and $a = 4, b = 6$ and $a = -2, b = 0$. Solving for c in each case (and rejecting the case that produces $c = 0 = b$), we get three triplets of points: $(3, -9), (10, -100), (-15, 225)$ and $(1, -1), (3, 9), (-6, -36)$ and $(4, -16), (6, -36), (-12, 144)$. In general, if a line crosses $y^2 = x^4$ in four lattice points whose abscissas are $a, b, c,$ and d, with $a < b < c < d$, we can show that $a + b + c + d = 0$ and $ab = -cd$.

III.   (1) This result comes from using the formula for the tangent of the angle between 2 lines together with the fact that the slopes of $\overleftrightarrow{AB}$ and $\overleftrightarrow{AD}$ are $(a + b)$ and $(a + d)$ respectively. (2) If $ABCD$ is cyclic, its opposite angles are supplementary. Then $\tan A = -\tan C$ implies $(a + b)(a + d) = (c + b)(c + d)$. Simplification leads to $a + b + c + d = 0$. An alternate, elegant proof: Algebraically solving $(x - h)^2 + (y - k)^2 = r^2$ and $y = x^2$ simultaneously, we simply substitute x^2 for y in the first equation. Without even multiplying out, we see that the resulting 4th degree polynomial equation in x would have no 3rd degree term. Thus the sum of its roots is 0. But those roots are the abscissas of the intersection points, namely $a, b, c,$ and d!! [Note: If the slopes of the successive sides are $m_1, m_2, m_3,$ and m_4, this is equivalent to several interesting relationships: $m_1 m_2 = m_3 m_4$; $m_2 m_3 = m_1 m_4$; $m_1 = -m_3, m_2 = -m_4$ (this relationship between opposite sides of the quadrilateral comes from the two previous relationships); $m_1 + m_2 + m_3 + m_4 = 0$. It can be shown in general that for 4 points on $y = px^2 + qx + r$ to be cyclic, the sum of their abscissas must be 4 times the abscissa of the vertex of the parabola. Try to show that no cyclic quadrilateral whose vertices are lattice points on $y = x^2$ can contain a right angle.] To prove the converse, note that each step of the previous proof can be reversed, leading to angles A and C being supplementary; thus the quadrilateral is cyclic. Note that these results hold even if the points are not lattice points. (3) Let the four abscissas be a, b, c, and k. Then $a + b + c + k = 0$ implies $k = -(a + b + c)$, which is clearly an integer. Thus the fourth point is (k, k^2), a lattice point. [A circle through three lattice points will not always intersect the parabola in a fourth point. In particular, if $a + b + 2c = 0$, the circle through A, B, and C will be tangent to the parabola at C! Here is a wonderful way to construct a tangent line to a "printed" parabola, $y = x^2$, at any point C on it, just using straight edge and compasses. Bisecting parallel chords of the parabola leads to a line parallel to the axis of symmetry. Construct a perpendicular to this, and drop a perpendicular to that last line from C (call its foot C'); on this same line, mark points P' and Q' on either side of C', so that $P'C' = C'Q'$. Now erect perpendiculars from P' and Q' to the parabola (meeting it at P and Q respectively, with abscissas p and q respectively). Since the slope of $\overline{PQ}$ is $p + q$, which equals $2c$, and the tangent to the parabola at C must have slope $2c$ (from calculus), a parallel to $\overline{PQ}$ through C will be the tangent line! Although this method is shown here only for the parabola $y = x^2$, it applies just as is for *any* "printed" parabola, since it can be shown that the slope of $\overline{PQ}$ must equal the slope of the tangent line at C.]

Team Questions

T1.   *Method 1*: The "average" number is clearly 33,333, so the sum is $120(33333) = 3999960$.

  Method 2: Each column in the sum contains 24 of each digit, so the sum is $24(1 + 2 + 3 + 4 + 5)(10000 + 1000 + 100 + 10 + 1) = 24(15)(11111) = 3999960$.

T2.   The coordinates of A and B must satisfy both equations, so they satisfy the difference of these equations, which is

$$10x - 10y - 71 = 0.$$

The slope of this line is 1. Alternatively, by completing squares, we can get the centers of the circles. The common chord will be perpendicular to the line joining those centers.

T3. Let the altitudes, each of length h, cut the longer base into seg-
     ments of lengths x, 3, and x. Comparing areas, $(1/2)hx = 3h$,
     which implies $x = 6$. The minimum perimeter occurs when
     each leg of the trapezoid equals $x + 1 = 7$ (since the sides are
     given to be integers). The minimum possible perimeter is thus
     $7 + 3 + 7 + 15 = 32$.

T4. Whenever $b^2 - 4ac$ is a square, we wish to have $144b^2 - 16kac$
     also a square. The latter expression is $144[b^2 - (k/9)ac]$, which
     will clearly always be a square if $k = 36$. The problem implies
     that this value is unique (for positive integer k). Although a
     demonstration of that is *not* called for, one (rather lengthy) way
     it can be shown is to compare two specific quadratic equations.
     For example, $(a, b, c) = (1, 6, 9)$ leads to $b^2 - (k/9)ac = 36 - k$;
     this is a square when $k = 36, 35, 32, 27, 20$, or 11. For $(a, b, c) =$
     $(3, 10, 3), b^2 - (k/9)ac = 100 - k$; this is a square when $k =$
     $100, 99, 96, 91, 84, 75, 64, 51, 36$, or 19. No value other than 36
     can work in both cases.

T5. The graph of
     $$y = \sin x° + \cos x°$$
     $$= \sqrt{2} \sin x° \cos 45° + \sqrt{2} \cos x° \sin 45° = \sqrt{2} \sin(x + 45)°$$

     is a sine curve that, in the given domain, reaches its maximum
     at $x = 45$. Comparing this graph with that of $y = \tan x°$, we
     see that the latter is lower at $x = 45$, but higher at $x = 60$.
     From the 3-4-5 triangle [whose acute angles are approximately
     $37°$ and $53°$], we see that $\tan 53° < \sin 53° + \cos 53°$. Equality
     occurs between $x = 53$ and $x = 60$, so $[x/10] = 5$. [In fact,
     equality actually occurs between $x = 54$ and $x = 54.5$.]

T6. Let P and Q be the midpoints of medians $\overline{AD}$ and $\overline{BE}$ respec-
     tively, and let the medians intersect at G. Letting $GD = 2x$,
     we have $AG = 4x, AP = 3x$, so $PG = x$. Since $\overline{PQ}$ is parallel
     to $\overline{AB}$, triangles PQG and ABG are similar, with ratio of simil-
     itude $1 : 4$. Thus the area of $PQG = (1/16)$ the area of ABG.
     Similarly, we see that the area of $PQR = (1/16)$ the area of
     $ABC = (1/16)(1024) = 64$.

T7. Changing the first factor to $(999999999999)/9$, we see that the
     radicand is

$$[(10^{12} - 1)/9][10^{12} + 5]+1 = [(10^{24} + 4 \cdot 10^{12} - 5)+9]/9$$

$$= (10^{24} + 4 \cdot 10^{12} + 4)/9$$

$$= (10^{12} + 2)^2/9.$$

Thus the square root is

$$(10^{12} + 2)/3 = (10^{12} - 1 + 3)/3$$

$$= (999999999999 + 3)/3 = 333333333334.$$

T8.   Drawing a unit circle around the origin O in the complex plane, we know that the points representing the nth roots of unity lie on this circle and are the vertices of a regular n-gon. The points P and Q, representing the complex numbers z and $z + 1$ respectively, lie on this circle; $\overline{PQ}$ is parallel to the x-axis (with P to the left of the y-axis), and $PQ = 1 = OP = OQ$, so angle $POQ = 60°$. Noticing the position of this central angle, we see that additional vertices of the n-gon must lie at $A(1,0), B(-1,0)$, and at points P' and Q' representing $-z$ and $-(z + 1)$ respectively, producing (so far) the six vertices of a regular hexagon. Notice that P, A, and Q' must represent the cube roots of 1, so $z^3 = 1$. If there are additional vertices along arc PQ, there must be corresponding vertices along each of the other five arcs of the circle. Thus n must be a multiple of 6. Since it is given to be a multiple of 5, the smallest possible value for n is 30, and $n + z^3 = 31$.

T9.   Let the points where circle Q meets the semicircle and $\overline{AB}$ be C and D respectively. Draw $\overline{QD}[= x], \overline{OQC}[= 1], \overline{PO}[= 1/2]$, $\overline{PQ}[= 1/2+x]$, and a perpendicular from Q to $\overline{PO}[= y]$ meeting $\overline{PO}$ at E. Note that $OQ = 1-x, EO = QD = x$, and $PE = 1/2-x$. Then $(1 - x)^2 - x^2 = y^2 = (1/2 + x)^2 - (1/2 - x)^2$, which implies that $1 - 2x = 2x$, so $x = 1/4$.

T10. Let $PQ = d$ and $d^2 = s$. We will find the distance between these skew lines by minimizing s. An arbitrary point P on the line $y = -x + 1$ (in the xy-plane) has coordinates $(x_1, -x_1 + 1, 0)$. An arbitrary point Q on the line $z = -2x + 1$ (in the xz-plane) has coordinates $(x_2, 0, -2x_2 + 1)$. The square of the distance between them is

$$s = (x_2 - x_1)^2 + (x_1 - 1)^2 + (-2x_2 + 1)^2$$

$$= 5x_2^2 + 2x_1^2 - 2x_1x_2 - 2x_1 - 4x_2 + 2$$

$$= 2x_1^2 - x_1(2x_2 + 2) + (5x_2^2 - 4x_2 + 2).$$

Temporarily thinking of Q as a fixed point, we have here a parabolic relationship between s and x_1. Since the turning point of the parabola $y = Ax^2 + Bx + C$ is at $(-\frac{B}{2A}, -\frac{B^2-4AC}{4A})$, our parabola has its (minimum) turning point when

$$s = -\frac{(2x_2 + 2)^2 - 8(5x_2^2 - 4x_2 + 2)}{8} = \frac{9}{2}x_2^2 - 5x_2 + \frac{3}{2}.$$

This gives the minimum s for any given x_2. Finally, we will allow Q its freedom, and find the value of x_2 that produces the smallest of all these s's. Since this last relationship is also parabolic, we have our minimum at $s = -\frac{25-27}{18} = \frac{1}{9}$, so $d = 1/3$.

Individual Questions

I1.   If my age now is x, then $(x - 21)(x + 21) = p^3$, which implies that $x - 21 = 1$ and $x + 21 = p^3$ [not acceptable, since x would equal 22] OR $x - 21 = p$ and $x + 21 = p^2$. The latter implies (by subtraction) that $p^2 - p = p(p - 1) = 42$, which implies that $p = 7$, so $x = 28$. Notice that this is a "perfect" age.

I2.   Given that the diagonals of the quadrilateral are perpendicular, $a^2 + c^2 = (p^2 + q^2) + (r^2 + s^2)$ and $b^2 + d^2 = (q^2 + r^2) + (s^2 + p^2)$, so $a^2 + c^2 = b^2 + d^2$! Then $2^2 + 9^2 = 6^2 + x^2$, so $x = 7$. It is interesting to prove that this theorem and its converse are true even for a concave quadrilateral or for a quadrilateral that is "self-intersecting"!

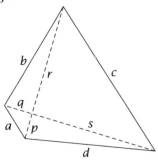

I3.   We have $100A + 10B + C = 22(A + B + C)$, leading to $26A = 4B + 7C$. Since $4B + 7C$ cannot exceed $36 + 63 (= 99)$, A cannot exceed 3. Trying $A = 3$, we quickly see that $B = 9$ and $C = 6$ lead to the greatest possible value, $n = 396$.

I4.   The total number of terms after the integer n has been listed n times is $1 + 2 + 3 + \cdots + n = n(n + 1)/2$. Seeking the greatest n such that $n(n + 1)/2 < 1992$, we have $n(n + 1) < 3984$. Trial quickly finds $n = 62$ [$62 \cdot 63 = 3906$, $63 \cdot 64 = 4032$], so the 1992nd term will be 63.

I5.   Let us examine the graph of $|x| + |y| = n$. In Quadrant I, this is (a segment of) the line $x + y = n$; in Quadrant II, it is (a segment of) the line $-x + y = n$; etc. The graph, for a fixed (positive) n, is a square with vertices on the axes. For each positive integer n, the graph contains 4 lattice points *on* the axes and $(n - 1)$ lattice points in each quadrant, for a total of $4(n - 1) + 4 \, [= 4n]$ lattice points all together. Then

$$L_1 - L_2 + L_3 - \cdots = 4(1 - 2 + 3 - \cdots + 999 - 1000)$$

$$= 4(-500) = -2000.$$

I6.   Drawing an altitude from the vertex angle, we have

$$\sin x = (1/2)\cos 7x / \cos x,$$

which implies that $2 \sin x \cos x = \cos 7x$, so $\sin 2x = \cos 7x$. Since $0 < x < 90$ and $\cos 7x$ must be positive, there are three possibilities: [Note: In the following, angles that are underlined are acute]

1. The inequalities $0 < 7x < 90$ imply that $\cos \underline{7x} = \sin \underline{2x}$. Thus $7x + 2x = 90$, so $x = 10$.

2. The inequalities $270 < 7x < 360$ [Note that $7x = 360$ doesn't work] imply that $\cos 7x = \cos \underline{(360 - 7x)} = \sin \underline{2x}$ [if $2x$ is acute] OR $\cos \underline{(360 - 7x)} = \sin \underline{(180 - 2x)}$ [if $2x$ is obtuse]. The former leads to $(360 - 7x) + 2x = 90$, so $x = 54$ [reject, since $2x$ is not acute]. The latter leads to $(360 - 7x) + (180 - 2x) = 90$, so $x = 50$.

3. The inequalities $360 < 7x < 450$ imply that $\cos 7x = \cos \underline{(7x - 360)} = \sin \underline{(180 - 2x)}$ [since $2x$ will be obtuse]. Thus $(7x - 360) + (180 - 2x) = 90$, so $x = 54$.

ANSWERS: 10, 50, 54. [Note: In cases (2) and (3), incorrectly accepting that $(360 - 7x) + 2x = 90$ and that $(7x - 360) + 2x = 90$, respectively, unfortunately produces the correct pair of answers (in the opposite order)!]

17.   "Completing the square" in $(x - [x])^2 - (x - [x]) + y^2 = 0$ produces $\left(x - [x] - \frac{1}{2}\right)^2 + y^2 = 1/4$, which is

$$\left(x - \left([x] + \frac{1}{2}\right)\right)^2 + y^2 = \frac{1}{4}.$$

Now examine what happens in the intervals $0 \le x < 1$, $1 \le x < 2$, $2 \le x < 3$, etc. (and also $-1 \le x < 0$, $-2 \le x < -1$, etc.). For each interval, we get a circle of radius $1/2$ with center at $([x] + \frac{1}{2}, 0)$. Thus the graph consists of a set of tangent congruent circles whose centers lie on the x-axis! The line $y = (1/5)x$ goes through both the origin and the point $(5/2, 1/2)$, which is the highest point of one of the circles; it intersects the first graph in 11 points [remember to count points to the left of the y-axis also!].

18.   We will solve this in general. Let $AD = a$, $AB = b$, $AE = c$, $AC = d$, $AF = x$, $AT = y$, and angle $BAT = $ angle $CAT = \theta$. Using K for area, we have $K_{DAE}/K_{BAC} = (K_{DAF} + K_{EAF})/(K_{BAT} + K_{CAT})$, which implies

$$\frac{1}{2}ac \sin 2\theta \Big/ \frac{1}{2}bd \sin 2\theta$$

$$= \left(\frac{1}{2}ax \sin \theta + \frac{1}{2}cx \sin \theta\right) \Big/ \left(\frac{1}{2}by \sin \theta + \frac{1}{2}dy \sin \theta\right).$$

Therefore we have $ac/bd = x(a + c)/y(b + d)$, so $x/y = ac(b + d)/bd(a + c)$ [nice formula!]. Thus $AF/AT = 5/18$ or $5 : 18$. Note that $x : y$ is *not* determined by simply giving the *ratios* of $a : b$ and $c : d$! [e.g. using $a = 1, b = 4$, compare the results of $c = 2, d = 6$ with $c = 1, d = 3$.]

Relay #1

R1-1. Since both 13 and 31 are primes, we need multiples of each whose difference is less than 5. We quickly find that 62 and 65 are the smallest positive integers satisfying this, so the consecutive integers are 61, 62, 63, 64, and 65.

R1-2. We have $T = 61$ and $K = 4$. Thus, $[(1-i)^2]^K = [-2i]^K = [-2i]^4 = 16$.

R1-3. We have $T = 16$. Since each side of the triangle can only be an edge, face diagonal, or "main" diagonal of the cube, the only possible perimeters are $T + T + T\sqrt{2} = T(2 + \sqrt{2})$, $T + T\sqrt{2} + T\sqrt{3} = T(1 + \sqrt{2} + \sqrt{3})$, or $T\sqrt{2} + T\sqrt{2} + T\sqrt{2} = T(3\sqrt{2})$. A comparison shows that the largest is $3T\sqrt{2} = 48\sqrt{2}$.

Relay #2

R2-1. Let n be the solution. If n has only two factors, it must be a prime; if n has an odd prime number of factors, it must be of the form p^{q-1}, p and q primes, q odd [the simplest case being p^2]. Checking the numbers 124, 123, 122, 121, we quickly find that the number $121 = 11^2$ has exactly three factors.

R2-2. We have $T = 121$ and $K = 11$. Thus $\log_4 n = (\log n)/(\log 4) = (\log n)/(2\log 2) = 1/[2(\log 2)/(\log n)] = 1/2K = 1/22$.

R2-3. We have $T = 1/22$ and $r = 22$. We find that

$$F(0) = 1,$$

$$F(1) = x \cdot 1 + 1 = x + 1,$$

$$F(2) = x(x + 1) + 1 = x^2 + x + 1,$$

$$\vdots$$

$$F(r) = x^r + x^{r-1} + \cdots + x + 1.$$

Thus $(x - 1) \cdot F(r) = x^{r+1} - 1 = x^{23} - 1$.

1993 American Regions Mathematics League Solutions

Power Question

I.   A1. $x_2 = 50.320000$, $x_{12} = 8.000000$; limiting value is 8 $[= \sqrt{64}]$.

        A2. $x_2 = 66.668800$, $x_{12} = 4.000001$; limiting value is 4 $[= \sqrt[3]{64}]$.

        A3. $x_2 = 8.944271$, $x_{12} = 4.000003$; limiting value is 4 $[= \sqrt[3]{64}]$.

In each case, the value of $x_1 [> 0]$ is arbitrary.

      B. $x_{n+1} = (1/5)[4x_n + (64/x_n^4)]$. In the limiting case, we set $x_{n+1} = x_n = k$, producing $k = (1/5)[4k + (64/k^4)]$, leading to $k^5 = 64$, so k is the 5th root of 64. Actually, we can use $x_{n+1} = (1/a)[(a-1)x_n + (64/x_n^4)]$.

II.   A.   We have $\cos(\theta/2) = \cos \angle NOP = d_{n+1}$. But $\cos(\theta/2) = \sqrt{(1 + \cos\theta)/2} = \sqrt{(1 + \cos \angle MOP)/2} = \sqrt{(1 + d_n)/2}$. There are other ways to prove this result although you were directed to this approach.

      B.   Since $\overline{PO}$ is a median of right triangle $A_{n+1}PQ$, area of $A_{n+1}PQ = 2(\text{area of } A_{n+1}PO)$. But [noting that $\overline{PM}$ is an altitude to hypotenuse $\overline{A_{n+1}Q}$] the area of $A_{n+1}PQ$ is $(1/2)(x_n)(2) = x_n$, and the area of $A_{n+1}PO$ is

$$(1/2)(d_{n+1})(2x_{n+1}) = d_{n+1}x_{n+1}.$$

Then $x_n = 2d_{n+1}x_{n+1}$ leads to the desired result. Other approaches may include use of the Pythagorean Theorem.

C. From section B,

$$S_n/d_{n+1} = \left(2^{n+1}x_n\right) / (x_n/2x_{n+1}) = 2^{n+2}x_{n+1} = S_{n+1}.$$

D. $S_1 = 2.8284\ldots$ [the following digits depend on how many places were used during the calculations], $S_7 = 3.1415\ldots$. We see that S_n is approaching π. Also, S_n is the sum of the lengths of a set of chords whose arcs always add up to half the circumference of the circle. As n increases, the number of chords doubles, each chord length getting closer to the length of its arc. The limiting value of S_n would be half the circumference of this circle of radius 1, which is π. [It would be interesting to continue the calculating of S_n for larger and larger values of n; "round off errors" may eventually lead to "chaos" rather than to π, even though the limit of S_n is indeed π!]

III. A. $1, 3, 4, 7, 11, 18, 29, 47$ [These are called Lucas numbers.]

B. $L_{n+1} = r^{n+1} + s^{n+1} = (r^n + s^n)(r + s) - rs(r^{n-1} + s^{n-1}) = L_n \cdot L_1 - (-1)(L_{n-1}) = L_n + L_{n-1}$.

C. $1.61, 2.61, 4.23, 6.85, 11.09, 17.94, 29.03, 46.97$. For odd n, $L_n = [r^n]$, where the brackets represent the Greatest Integer Function; for even n, $L_n = [r^n + 1]$ OR $L_n = [r^n + \frac{1}{2}]$ for $n > 1$, $L_1 = 1$ OR L_n is the closest integer to r^n for $n > 1$, $L_1 = 1$ etc.

D. 43 digits. [$L_{201} \approx r^{201} \approx 1.0151 \times 10^{42}$, which has 43 digits.]

E. $n = 96$ [Suppose $r^n \geq 10^{20}$. Then $n \log r \geq 20$, and $n \geq 20/\log r \approx 95.6$. The smallest such n is 96. One can check by raising r to the 96th power, then to the 95th power.]; $n = 953$ [Checking this may well exceed the capacity of your calculator! Other methods for checking can be developed.]

F. In a manner similar to the above, we can show that $F_n \approx r^n/\sqrt{5}$. Then $r^n/\sqrt{5} \geq 10^{20}$ implies $n \log r - (1/2)\log 5 \geq 20$, so $n \geq [20 + (1/2)\log 5]/\log r \approx 97.3$, and the smallest such n is 98. Since $r^{98}/\sqrt{5} \approx 1.3530 \times 10^{20}$, the first four digits of F_{98} are 1353.

Team Questions

T1. Number the columns 1-5 *from right to left.* Clearly there is a carry into columns 4 and 5. Then $A + 1 = U + 10$, so $A = U + 9$, so $A = 9$, $U = 0$, $Y = L + 1$. From column 1, either $Y + L = A = 9$ or $Y + L = A + 10 = 19$ (impossible), so $L = 4$ and $Y = 5$. From columns 2 and 3, either $R + I = C$ and $R + G = C + 10$ (leading to $G - I = 10$; impossible) or $R + I = C + 10$ and $R + G + 1 = C + 10$ (leading to $I = G + 1$); note here that $R + G$ is greater than 10 and $C = R + I - 10$. Finally we consider the remaining possibilities for G [1, 2, 3, 6, 7, 8], which determine I, R, and C; we very quickly find the only possibilities lead to $(I, R) = (3, 8)$ or $(8, 3)$, both producing $C = 1$. Thus YUCCA is 50,119.

T2. Let the diagonals intersect at P, and let θ be the obtuse angle formed at P. [A similar argument will hold if θ is the acute angle, but both angles have the same sine.] An altitude from P to the longer side of the rectangle forms a right triangle with legs of $3/2$ and $1/2$, and containing an acute angle $\phi(= \theta/2)$ at P. Now $\sin \theta = \sin 2\phi = 2 \sin \phi \cos \phi = 2(3/\sqrt{10})(1/\sqrt{10}) = 6/10 = 3/5$ or .6. Generally, if the sides of the rectangle are a and b, $\sin \theta = 2ab/(a^2 + b^2)$. One can also prove this by using the Law of Sines on one of the small triangles formed.

T3. Let Arctan $(1/3) = \theta$; then

$$\tan 2\theta = 2(\tan \theta)/(1 - \tan^2 \theta) = 2(1/3)/[1 - (1/9)] = 3/4.$$

Now

$$\text{Arctan } x = \text{Arctan } 1 + 2 \text{ Arctan } (1/3) = 45° + 2\theta.$$

"Taking the tangent of each side" produces

$$x = [1 + \tan 2\theta]/[1 - (1)(\tan 2\theta)] = [1 + (3/4)]/[1 - (3/4)] = 7.$$

Other methods may lead to additional values for x, which are extraneous.

T4. We have $\frac{10!}{3!5!} = {}_{10}P_x = \frac{10!}{(10-x)!}$, so $3!5! = 6 \cdot 5! = 6! = (10 - x)!$, leading to $x = 4$. [Miscellaneous note: $3!5! = 6!$ is an example of $a!b! = c!$. Aside from the "trivial" examples of this (where $a = 0$ or 1 and $b = c$), and the "semi-trivial" ones (like $3!5! = 6 \cdot 5! = 6!$, $4!23! = 24 \cdot 23! = 24!$, $5!119! = 120 \cdot 119! = 120!$, etc.), is $6!7! = 10!$ truly the only non-trivial example?]

T5. Draw $\overline{PT}$ and note that $\overline{AB}$ is perpendicular to $\overline{AC}$, $\overline{PT}$ is perpendicular to $\overline{TB}$, $AP = PT = 1$, and $PB = 3$. Then $\tan B = 1/\sqrt{8} = AC/4$, so $AC = \sqrt{2}$.

T6. Noting that $x^3 + y^3 = (x + y)(x^2 - xy + y^2)$, we have

$$(7^4)^3 + (4^4)^3 = (7^4 + 4^4)(7^8 - 7^4 \cdot 4^4 + 4^8).$$

The first factor equals 2,657 (if this were not a prime, it would have to be the product of two 4-digit primes, which is impossible). Incidentally, the second factor turns out to be $2617 \cdot \underline{1993}$!!

T7. The totals will be the integers from 2 through 12, occurring with probabilities $1/36$, $2/36, \ldots, 5/36$, $6/36$, $5/36, \ldots, 2/36$, $1/36$ respectively. Since these can occur in 11! permutations, we see that the probability is $11!(1/36)(2/36) \cdots (5/36)(6/36)(5/36) \cdots (2/36)(1/36) = 11!6!5!/36^{11}$. Thus (a, b, c, d) is $(5, 6, 11, 11)$.

T8. If M is the mean of the entire set, and M' is the mean of the first set, then $kM' + 7k(4M') = 8kM$, whereupon $29M' = 8M$. Thus (the integer) M is at least 29. For example, since M' is at least 8, we could have the sets $\{8\}$ and $\{32, 32, 32, 32, 32, 32, 32\}$.

T9. From similar triangles, $r/d = x/a$ and $R/d = x/b = x/(d - a)$. Solving each for a leads to $x = Rr/(R + r)$. [This is a famous result. It is usually presented as two wires, each going from the top of one pole to the bottom of the other; if the heights of the poles are given, find the height of the point where the wires cross. (See figure on top of next page.) The answer is independent of the distance between the poles! We are extending the setting to three dimensions.] If the areas of the bases of the cones are K and k, then the area of C is

$$\begin{aligned}
\pi x^2 &= \pi[Rr/(R + r)]^2 \\
&= \pi[(\sqrt{K/\pi})(\sqrt{k/\pi})/(\sqrt{K/\pi} + \sqrt{k/\pi})]^2 \\
&= [(\sqrt{K})(\sqrt{k})/(\sqrt{K} + \sqrt{k})]^2.
\end{aligned}$$

[Note the similarity to the formula for x. The area of C is independent of the height of the cones!] Thus the area of C is $[30 \cdot 20/(30 + 20)]^2 = 144$.

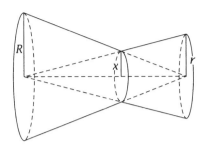
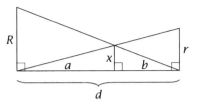

T10. [Trying small values of a, b, and c could quickly lead to the conclusion that $(a, b, c) = (n, n + 2, n + 3)$ only. Here is a proof, however.] From $F_c - F_b = F_b - F_a$ we get $F_c = F_b + (F_b - F_a)$, which is less than $F_b + F_{b+1}$, which equals F_{b+2}. Since F_c is greater than F_b, we must have $F_c = F_{b+1}$. Then

$$F_a = F_b + F_b - F_c = F_b + (F_b - F_{b+1}) = F_b - F_{b-1} = F_{b-2},$$

so the sequence must be of the form F_n, F_{n+2}, F_{n+3} [the only exception is F_2, F_3, F_4 which is identical to F_1, F_3, F_4]. Finally, $(a) + (a + 2) + (a + 3) = 2000$ implies that $a = 665$. Note that F_n, F_{n+2}, F_{n+3}, F_x cannot be in arithmetic sequence, since the last three subscripts do not fit the required pattern. Thus no four Fibonacci numbers can form an arithmetic sequence!

Individual Questions

I1.   We have $y^2 = (x + 1)^2$ which implies [for positive y] that $y = x + 1$. Letting x go from 1,994 to 2,018 produces 25 ordered pairs.

I2.   Drop a perpendicular, $\overline{CP}$, from C to the x-axis; call the origin O. From congruent triangles AOD and DPC, $OD = PC = 8$, so $DP = 5$. By the Pythagorean Theorem, $CD^2 = 89$, which is the area of the square.

I3.   The mean is $(28 + x)/5$. If $x \geq 6$, median $= 6$, so $(28 + x)/5 = 6$ produces $x = 2$ (contradiction); if $4 < x < 6$, median $= x$, so $(28 + x)/5 = x$ produces $x = 7$ (contradiction); if $x \leq 4$, median $= 4$ leads to $x = -8$.

I4.   Let the pentagon be *ABCDE*.

   1. If the perpendicular diagonals meet *at* a vertex, say *A*,
       then $\sphericalangle CAD = 90°$ and $AC < CD$; then in triangle *ABC*,
       since $AB = CB = CD$, angle *B* will be less than 60° and
       base angle *BAC* will be greater than 60°. By similar rea-
       soning, angle *EAD* will be greater than 60°, so angle *EAB*
       will be reflex (contradiction).

   2. Assume $\overline{AC}$ is perpendicular to $\overline{BE}$, intersecting at *P*. Draw
       $\overline{CE}$. Clearly $AP = PC$ and $BP = PE$. Then *ABCE* is a rhom-
       bus, so $BC = EC = ED = DC$ (and triangle *CDE* is equilat-
       eral). If $\sphericalangle B = 100°$, the other angles of the pentagon are
       140°, 60°, 160°, 80° (any order is acceptable). If $\sphericalangle BCD =$
       100°, then $\sphericalangle BCE = 40°$, so $\sphericalangle AED = 140° + 60° = 200°$
       (contradiction). Note that a convex equilateral pentagon
       with two perpendicular diagonals *must* contain a 60° an-
       gle (and it will be the smallest angle)!

I5.   Note that

$$\cos 16° \sin 7° < \sin 7° < \sin 9°,$$

$$\sin 9° = \sin 16° \cos 7° - \cos 16° \sin 7°,$$

   and

$$\cos 67° = \sin 23° = \sin 16° \cos 7° + \cos 16° \sin 7°.$$

   Thus

$$\cos 16° \sin 7° < \sin 9° < \sin 16° \cos 7° < \cos 67°,$$

   and the answer is $\cos 16° \sin 7°$, $\sin 9°$, $\sin 16° \cos 7°$, $\cos 67°$
   (this order is required!).

I6.   Expanding $(4A0 + 1)^{1A4}$ by the binomial theorem produces
       $(4A0)^{1A4} + 1A4 (4A0)^{1A3} (1) + \cdots + 1A4 (4A0) (1)^{1A3} + (1)^{1A4}$.
       The only term that affects the tens digit is $1A4 (4A0) (1)^{1A3}$,
       since all previous terms end in at least two zeros; this term
       has a tens digit determined by $4 \cdot A$. Given that $4 \cdot A$ ends in a 2,
       A must be 3 or 8 (both required).

I7.   Factoring produces

$$x^{98}(x^2 - 4^x) - (x^2 - 4^x) = (x^{98} - 1)(x^2 - 4^x) = 0,$$

so $x^{98} = 1$ or $x^2 = 4^x$. The first has exactly two real solutions $[\pm 1]$. The second has only one real solution, as is quickly seen from sketching $y = x^2$ and $y = 4^x$ on the same axes; the graphs clearly cross in quadrant II, while in quadrant I both are increasing but never cross. The answer is 3. It would be a bit harder to analyze the number of real solutions to $x^2 = 3^x$, and still harder for $x^2 = 2^x$ (could $y = x^2$ and $y = 2^x$ possibly cross again *between* $x = 2$ and $x = 4$?).

I8.   Let $N = \text{ABCDE} = 10000A + 1000B + 100C + 10D + E$ be a 5-digit multiple of p. Then p must also divide $N' = \text{EABCD}$, and (since p is greater than 10) p divides $10N' = 100000E + 10000A + 1000B + 100C + 10D = 99999E + N$. Thus p divides $99999E$, so it must divide 99999 [$= 3 \cdot 3 \cdot 41 \cdot 271$]. Thus p must be 271. Reversing our argument, if 271 divides N, it divides $N + 99999E$, so it divides N'. Note how the prime factors of $10^5 - 1$ are key to the solution for a 5-digit number. Here is the start of a chart showing the primes p for which any n-digit multiple of p remains a multiple of p under cyclic permutation:

n	2	3	4	5	6
p	$3, 11$	$3, 37$	$3, 11, 101$	$3, 41, 271$	$3, 7, 13, 37$

Relay #1

R1-1. If $n/(A + B + C) = k$, then $kA + kB + kC = n = 100A + 10B + C$, which implies $k \le 100$. [The number 100 occurs if $B = C = 0$].

R1-2. We have $T = 100$. This is $(9 \cdot 13 \cdot 17)^T \cdot 13 \cdot 17 \cdot 17$, which has the same units digit as $9^T \cdot 7$. If T is odd, 9^T ends in 9, so the answer is 3; if T is even, 9^T ends in 1, so the answer is 7. A student experienced in relays will immediately pass back one of these answers, even before knowing T! At best, the third member of the relay team will thus solve the final problem very quickly; at worst, a change of answer will be passed back shortly.

R1-3. We have $T = 7$. The six small circles must be "consecutively tangent" and would exactly fit around the outside of another circle of radius r. Then the radius of the large circle is $3r = 3T$, so $r = T = 7$.

Relay #2

R2-1. From $b \log a = a \log b$, we find that $a^b = b^a$. Clearly 2 and 4 satisfy this equation (and the problem implies that there is only one value for $ab + 1$) in either order, so $ab + 1 = 9$. [Can you prove that no other unequal positive integers satisfy the equation?]

R2-2. We have $T = 9$. The coordinates of A and B are (a, a) and $(b, 8b)$ respectively. The slope of $\overline{AB} = T = (8b - a)/(b - a)$, so $8b - a = Tb - Ta$ which implies that $b(8 - T) = a(1 - T)$, so $b/a = (T - 1)/(T - 8) = 8$.

R2-3. We have $T = 8$. Dividing through by b^2 produces $(a/b)^2 + T = 6a/b$. Letting $a/b = x$, we have $x^2 - 6x + T = 0$. Thus the larger value of x is $3 + \sqrt{9 - T} = 4$.

1994 American Regions Mathematics League Solutions

Power Question

1.   (a) 0
    (b) 3
    (c) 99
    (d) 29.

    The first three examples, and a translation of the fourth to the origin, indicate that $N(l)$ for the segment joining (a, b) and (c, d) is 1 less than the greatest common divisor of $(a - c)$ and $(b - d)$.

2. Note that this solution is for an *oblique* segment.

    (a) Any positioning of the segment is essentially equivalent to positioning it from $(0, 0)$ to $(5, 12)$, so $N(13) = 0$.

    (b) Extending the $l = 13$ segment to 4 times its length produces $N(52) = 3$.

    (c) This segment is 5 times a segment of length 13, so $N(l) = 4$, OR 13 times a segment of length 5, so $N(l) = 12$; but it can also be positioned as the hypotenuse of a primitive Pythagorean right triangle (either the $16 - 63 - 65$ triangle or the $33 - 56 - 65$ triangle), producing $N(l) = 0$. Thus the answers are 0, 4, and 12. The sides of such primitive triangles are found by using the well-known expressions for them: $m^2 - n^2$, $2mn$, and $m^2 + n^2$ (in this case using $m = 8$, $n = 1$, or $m = 7$, $n = 4$).

3. We see that $N(l)$ can be $13 \cdot 17 - 1 (= 220)$, $5 \cdot 17 - 1 (= 84)$, $5 \cdot 13 - 1 (= 64)$, $17 - 1 (= 16)$, $13 - 1 (= 12)$, $5 - 1 (= 4)$, or 0 (when $l = 1105$ is the hypotenuse of a primitive right triangle). The answer is 7. Try extending this to the product of r distinct primes, each of the form $4k + 1$ (only these primes and their multiples can be the hypotenuses of integer-sided right triangles, and can therefore represent oblique lattice segments); then consider products of other types.

4. The area of the triangle [using determinants, or Hero's Formula (the sides of the triangle are $50 - 130 - 80\sqrt{2}$), or enclosing it in a rectangle, etc.] is 2800, and $B = 100$, so $I = 2751$.

5. (a) The answer is 624 [to maximize I, we minimize B by placing two of the vertices at $(0, 0)$ and $(24, 7)$; other positions of the square yield $I = 616$ or 576].

   (b) The answer is 673 [the only other value of I is 625]. If the side is the integer n, then $(n - 1)^2 \leq I \leq n^2 - 1$; the minimum occurs for a square that is not oblique.

6. The third side must be between $13 - 5$ and $13 + 5$, so we need only try integers from 9 through 17. Of these, only 10, 13, 15, and 17 are possible [see solution to (3), above]. In each case, the area is irrational, but Pick's Theorem (for example) shows that a lattice polygon must have a rational area. Even if a triangle is Heronian (integer sides and area) and each side is a multiple of a prime of the form $4k + 1$, it may not be possible to make it an *oblique* lattice triangle (e.g., try to place the 13-13-10 triangle obliquely). We can also show that an equilateral triangle can not be a lattice triangle (in the coordinate plane; it *can* be placed on lattice points in 3 dimensions).

7. (a) The coordinates of all lattice points fit one of the following patterns: (odd, odd) (odd, even) (even, odd) (even, even). Let us refer to these patterns as α, β, γ, and δ, *in any order*. Given five lattice points, at least two of them must fit the same pattern, in which case their midpoint must also be a lattice point.

   (b) Let the pentagon be $ABCDE$. At least two vertices must fit the same pattern; if they are non-successive vertices, their midpoint is an interior lattice point. If they are successive vertices [e.g., $A = \alpha$ and $B = \beta$], then there is another lattice point (call it F) on $\overline{AB}$; if $F = \alpha$, there is another lattice point on $\overline{AF}$; continuing this process shows that eventually we get a point Q on $\overline{AB}$ for which $Q \neq \alpha$ [suppose $Q = \beta$]. Now vertices C and E cannot match α or β [else the theorem follows from (7a)]. Let $C = \gamma$ and $E = \delta$. Finally, if vertex $D = \alpha$ or β, the theorem again follows from (7a). If $D = \gamma$ (for example), there is a point R on $\overline{CD}$ such that $R \neq \gamma$. Whatever other pattern R fits will produce an interior lattice point.

(c1) Call the trapezium $ABCD$, and let lattice points Q and R be on $\overline{AB}$ and $\overline{BC}$, respectively. Then pentagon $AQRCD$ must contain an interior lattice point [by 7(b)].

(c2) Call the trapezium $ABCD$, and let there be no lattice points on $\overline{BC}$ and $\overline{AD}$ (other than the endpoints). Assume that $\angle B + \angle C > 180°$ [if $B + C < 180°$ and $A + D < 180°$, then the sum of all four angles is less than $360°$]. Consider rays $\overrightarrow{BA}$ and $\overrightarrow{CD}$ and the region between these diverging rays, but on that side of $\overline{AD}$ that does not include $\overline{BC}$; call that region L. Choose lattice point P in L such that no other lattice point in L is closer to $\overline{AD}$. Draw $\overline{PA}$ and $\overline{PD}$. There is no lattice point in triangle PAD (else it would be closer to $\overline{AD}$ than P), yet there must be a lattice point inside of pentagon $PABCD$. Since that lattice point is not on $\overline{AD}$, it must be in the trapezium. [There are other ways to prove "Theorem 7c".]

8. Let the two sides be s and t, with $st = Q$ [a prime], and let the area be K [a prime].

Method 1: Let the vertices of the triangle be at $(0,0)$, (a,b), and (c,d). Using determinants, we find that $K = |(ad - bc)/2|$, so $|ad - bc| = 2K$. Furthermore, $Q^2 = (a^2 + b^2)(c^2 + d^2) =$ [by a well-known identity] $(ad - bc)^2 + (ac + bd)^2 =$ [using r for $(ac + bd)$] $(2K)^2 + r^2$. Therefore Q must be the hypotenuse of a primitive right triangle whose legs are $2K$ and r. Then $2K = 2mn$ [see (2c)], which implies $m = K$, $n = 1$ and $Q = m^2 + n^2 = K^2 + 1$. If K is an odd prime, Q is even and greater than 2 [this is impossible since Q is a prime]. Therefore K is an even prime, so $K = 2$, and $Q = 5$. There are only four such triangles [$5 - 1 - 2\sqrt{5}, 5 - 1 - 4\sqrt{2}, \sqrt{5} - \sqrt{5} - 2$, and $\sqrt{5} - \sqrt{5} - 4$].

Method 2: Let θ be the angle included between sides s and t. From $K = st(\sin\theta)/2$, we find that $\sin\theta = 2K/st = 2K/Q$.

Since st is an integer, the Law of Cosines shows that $\cos \theta$ must be rational. Thus

$$\cos \theta = \pm\sqrt{1 - \sin^2 \theta} = \pm\sqrt{1 - (2K/Q)^2} = \pm\sqrt{Q^2 - (2K)^2}/Q$$

implies that $Q^2 - (2K)^2$ must be a square, say r^2. The proof now continues as in Method 1 [Therefore Q must ...].

Team Questions

T1.   Adding $10x$ to both sides produces $(x + 1)^5 = 10(x + 1)$, so $(x + 1)^4 = 10$. Another approach is to bring everything to the left and divide by $x + 1$. This produces $x^4 + 4x^3 + 6x^2 + 4x - 9 = 0$, and adding 10 gives $(x + 1)^4 = 10$.

T2.   *Method 1*: From $k = \sin \theta = \frac{R-r}{R+r}$, we find that

$$\frac{r}{R} = \frac{1 - k}{1 + k} = \frac{1 - (1/2)}{1 + (1/2)} = \frac{1}{3}.$$

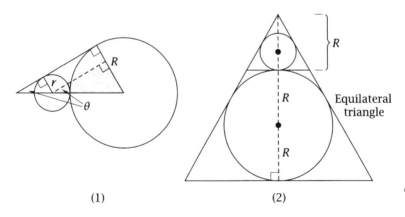

(1)   (2)   Equilateral triangle

Method 2: The ratio of similitude of the triangles is [from their heights] $1 : 3$, so the ratio of the inradii is $1 : 3$.

T3.   This becomes $b^n + (b + 1)^n = (b + 2)^n$. According to "Fermat's Last Theorem", the equation $x^n + y^n = z^n$ (where x, y, z, and n are positive integers) has no solutions for $n > 2$. This has certainly been established for $3 \le n \le 100$ (and far beyond), so our equation can only have solutions for $n = 2$ (specifically, $b = 3$). The answer to the problem is 1.

In 1994, Professor Andrew Wiles may perfect his (almost completed) proof of the general theorem, a problem that has eluded the best mathematicians for over 300 years!

T4. Note that this median and altitude cannot come from the same vertex. Let the triangle be ABC, with $AB = AC$.

Case 1: Let the altitude be $\overline{AH}$, and medians $\overline{BQ}$ and $\overline{CR}$ meet at P. Since $\overline{AH}$ must also be a median, $PH = 8$ and $CP = 10$. Then $CH = 6$ and the area of ABC is $(24)(12)/2 = 144$.

Case 2: Let the median be $\overline{AM}$, let an altitude be $\overline{BS}$, and let $CM = x$. Then, since $\overline{AM}$ must also be an altitude, we have $AC = \sqrt{x^2 + 225}$. Using two approaches to the area of triangle ABC, we have $24\sqrt{x^2 + 225} = 15(2x)$, so $x = 20$, and the area of triangle $ABC = 300$. Either answer is acceptable. At times, one approach to a problem is easier than another, but deciding which is easier can be a difficult decision in itself. Try this problem given a median and an angle-bisector; one approach leads to an unsolvable situation!

T5. Two different values of t must produce the same (x, y); call them t_1 and t_2. Then $(t_2)^2 - 2 = (t_1)^2 - 2$, so $t_2 = \pm t_1$ which implies that $t_2 = -t_1$. Now $(t_1)^3 - 9(t_1) + 5 = (-t_1)^3 - 9(-t_1) + 5$, so $(t_1)^3 = 9(t_1)$, which implies that $t_1 = 0, \pm 3$. If $t_1 = 0$, then $t_2 = 0$ (reject). Therefore $t_1 = 3$ and $t_2 = -3$ (or vice-versa), from which we can conclude that $(x, y) = (7, 5)$. Try drawing the graph.

T6. Since $y = x(ax + 19)$, y can be prime only if $x = 1$ and $ax + 19 = a + 19$ is prime OR $x = p$ [prime] and $ax + 19 = ap + 19 = 1$, which implies that $p = -18/a$. Thus we must make both $-18/a$ and $a + 19$ primes at the same time. [Note: If x equals a second prime, q ($\neq p$), then $q = -18/a = p$, which is a contradiction. Also, if $a = 0$, $y = 19x$ which cannot be prime for two different positive integers x.] Now $-18/a$ is prime only for $a = -6$ and -9; only $a = -6$ also makes $a + 19$ prime. The lattice points are then $(1, 13)$ and $(3, 3)$.

T7. [This problem is based on the first "knot" in *A Tangled Tale* by Lewis Carroll, the author of "Alice in Wonderland", and a well-known mathematician (real name, Charles Dodgson).] Let u be the sum of the uphill distances from A to B, let d be the sum of the downhill distances, and let v be the sum of the level distances. The total time is

$$(u/40 + d/60 + v/x) + (u/60 + d/40 + v/x) = 3,$$

so $ux + dx + 48v = 72x$. Hence $u + d = (72x - 48v)/x = 72 - v(48/x)$ and so $u + d + v = 72 - v[(48/x) - 1]$. Since v is not determined, we can only find $u + d + v$ if $(48/x) - 1 = 0$, so $x = 48$. In general, if the uphill and downhill rates are r_u and r_d respectively, and the total time is T, then $x = 2r_u r_d/(r_u + r_d)$ [the harmonic average of r_u and r_d], and the distance from A to B is $T(x/2)$.

T8.   Let point A_1 be on $\overline{B_0 C_0}$, and compare angles $B_1 A_1 C_1 [\sphericalangle A_1]$ and $B_0 A_0 C_0 [\sphericalangle A_0]$. We have

$$\sphericalangle A_1 \doteq (1/2) \; \overset{\frown}{B_1 C_1} \doteq (180 - \sphericalangle A_0)/2 = 90 - (\sphericalangle A_0/2).$$

Thus, starting with the "worst case scenario", in which $\sphericalangle A_0$ is slightly less than $180°$, we successively obtain angles $A_1 \approx 0°$, $A_2 \approx 90°$, $A_3 \approx 45°$, $A_4 \approx 67.5°$, $A_5 \approx 56.25°$, $A_6 \approx 61.875°$, and $A_7 \approx 59.0625°$. Thus, for any triangle $A_0 B_0 C_0$, triangle $A_7 B_7 C_7$ is "almost equilateral"! The answer is $n = 7$.

T9.   We have $xy + y = 4x^2 + Nx + N$, which implies that

$$4x^2 + (N - y)x + (N - y) = 0,$$

so

$$x = [y - N \pm \sqrt{(N - y)^2 - 16(N - y)}]/8.$$

All real values of y are possible except when

$$(N - y)(N - y - 16) < 0,$$

whereupon EITHER $(N - y) > 0$ and $(N - y - 16) < 0$ which implies $N - 16 < y < N$ OR $(N - y) < 0$ and $(N - y - 16) > 0$ which implies $N - 16 > y > N$ (impossible). For the interval $N - 16 < y < N$ to be of the required form, we need $(N - 16) = -(N)$, so $N = 8$. This is another nice graph to draw.

T10. This solution is based on the easily proved theorem that given rectangle $ABCD$ and point P, then $PA^2 + PC^2 = PB^2 + PD^2$;

this holds even when P is not in the plane of the rectangle! Let the vertices of one face of the box be A, B, C, and D, and the diagonally opposite vertices (with respect to the center of the box) be A', B', C', and D' respectively. To simplify notation, let the distance PA be represented simply by A, PB by B, etc. Thus we know that $A^2 + C^2 = B^2 + D^2$, and (from rectangle $ABA'B'$) $A^2 + A'^2 = B^2 + B'^2$, etc.

1. Let $A[= PA] = 1$. Then either $2 = B$ or $2 = C$ [$2 \neq A'$ since $A^2 + A'^2 = 1^2 + 2^2 < 3^2 +$ anything, so no distance from P to another vertex can equal the 3]. Suppose $2 = C$. Then $3 \neq A, C, B, D, A'$, or C'. Therefore $3 = B'$ or D' (symmetrical situation). Let $3 = B'$. Then $4 \neq A, C, B, D, A', C'$, or B', so $4 = D'$. But now we cannot accommodate a distance greater than 5. Therefore $2 = B$.

2. Now $3 \neq A, B, A'$, or B', so either $3 = C$ [or D'] or $3 = D$ [or C']. Suppose $3 = C$. Then we have $D = \sqrt{6}$. Now $4 \neq A', B', C'$, or D', since we could not accommodate a distance greater than 5. Therefore $3 = D$.

3. Finally, we have $C = \sqrt{12}$ and $4 = C'$ [this is the only way to get a pair of "opposite points" whose squares total more than 25]. Then $D' = \sqrt{19}$, $B' = \sqrt{24}$, and $A' = \sqrt{27}$ or $3\sqrt{3}$. Note: It can be shown that such a box *does* exist.

Individual Questions

I1.   Since 14 red squares (seven pairs) coincide, there are six reds that fall on white squares. This leaves $44 - 6 = 38$ white squares that coincide, or 19 pairs.

I2.   From congruent triangles RSD and PQB, $PB = 3$; therefore $AB = 11$. Draw a perpendicular from R to $\overline{AB}$, meeting $\overline{AB}$ at T; $AT = 3$, so $TP = 5$, so (in right triangle RTP) $RT = 12$. Area of $ABCD = 11 \cdot 12 = 132$.

I3.   For large n, $\sqrt{(n-5)^2 + 4}$ is fractionally more than $(n-5)$; therefore the answer is 19,941,989. In fact, this is true for $n \geq 7$.

I4.   Draw $\overline{QE}, \overline{AE}$, and $\overline{PE}$, and let $QA = p$, $PA = q$, and $AE = x$. Note that the circle with $\overline{AB}$ as diameter passes through E, and

$\overset{\frown}{AE}$ would be 1/4 of that circle. Thus angle $P = 45°$, regardless of the position of P on the semicircle! In a similar way, angle $Q = 45°$, so triangle QEP is an isosceles right triangle! Noting that $QE = (p+q)/\sqrt{2}$, and applying the Law of Cosines to triangle AQE, we get $x^2 = (p^2+q^2)/2$ [nice theorem for an isosceles right triangle!], so $x = 17$.

I5.   The most efficient method uses the fact that any number is congruent to the sum of its digits (mod 9). Realizing that $A + B + \cdots + H + I = 45 - J$, we have $45 - J \equiv 6 + J \pmod{9}$, which implies that $2J \equiv -6 \equiv 3 \equiv 12 \pmod{9}$, so $J = 6$. In fact, there are 360 different sets of addends that satisfy this problem (or 432 sets if we permit 0 to be the first digit of an addend)!

I6.   Consider the decagon in the complex plane. If it were translated so that its center were at the origin, the vertices would represent the roots of $f(x) = x^{10} - 1 = 0$. Since the P_n are each 2 more than the roots of $f(x) = 0$, they would be the roots of $f(x - 2) = 0$, which is $(x-2)^{10} - 1 = 0$. The product of these roots is (constant term/coefficient of x^{10}) $= 1023$.

I7.   Let the radius of the circle be $r\,(= 1994)$, so the point is $(2r, 2r)$. The slope of the radius to (a, b) is b/a, so the slope of the tangent is $-a/b$. Thus $-a/b = (2r - b)/(2r - a)$. Hence $2r(a + b) = a^2 + b^2 = r^2$ and so $a + b = r/2 = 997$.

I8.   If there are n coins, their total value is $2^0 + 2^1 + \cdots + 2^{n-1}$, which is $2^n - 1$. Now $5 \mid (2^n - 1)$ implies that $2^n \equiv 1 \pmod 5$ from which we conclude that $4 \mid n$. Thus n must be 32. Now

$$2^{32} - 1 = (2^{16} + 1)(2^{16} - 1)$$

$$= (2^{16} + 1)(2^8 + 1)(2^8 - 1)$$

$$= \cdots = (2^{16} + 1)(2^8 + 1)(2^4 + 1)(2^2 + 1)(2 + 1)(2 - 1).$$

Dividing by 5 [$= 2^2 + 1$], and noting that $2 - 1 = 1$, the value of the lost coins was $(2^{16} + 1)(2^8 + 1)(2^4 + 1)(2 + 1)$. When multiplied out, but still written as powers of 2, the product consists of 16 distinct addends. That means that the product, if written in base 2, would be a number with 16 1's, so it represents 16 coins.

Relay #1

R1-1. Since $3(13) = 39$ and $2(19) = 38$, $n = (3)(2)(37) = 222$.

R1-2. We have $T = 222$ and $N = 2$. Then

$$2^N + 2^{2N} + 2^{3N} = 2^N(1 + 2^N + 2^{2N}).$$

The second factor is odd and equals 21.

R1-3. We have $T = 21$. The expression on the left equals $(n + 1)! - 1$ [nicely proved by mathematical induction, among other ways], so $n + 1 = T$, and $n = T - 1 = 20$.

Relay #2

R2-1. We see that $n = a^2 - 124 = b^2 - 56$, so $a^2 - b^2 = 68$, which implies that $(a + b)(a - b) = 4 \cdot 17$. Since $(a + b)$ and $(a - b)$ have the same parity, we must have $(a + b)(a - b) = 34 \cdot 2$. Hence $a + b = 34$, $a - b = 2$ and so $a = 18$ and $n = 200$. Trying $a + b = -34$, $a - b = -2$ and other similar variations leads to the same value for a^2 in every case. Of course, the problem implies that there is only one answer.

R2-2. We have $T = 200$ and $d = 4$. Area of $BMC = (1/2)(d)(29)$; area of $ABC = (2)(\text{Area of } BMC) = 116$.

R2-3. We have $T = 116$. Draw a perpendicular from the origin, O, to the line $[y = (-5/2)x + 997]$, crossing the circle at $P(a, b)$. The slope of $\overline{OP} = 2/5$, so $b/a = 2/5$. Then

$$x^2 + y^2 = a^2 + b^2 = a^2 + (4a^2/25) = 29a^2/25 = T$$

so $a^2 = 25T/29 = 25 \cdot 116/29 = 100$. Hence $a = 10$, so $b = 2a/5 = 4$. Answer: $(10, 4)$, which is our symbolic way of signing off [from Larry and Gil, ending their principal authorship of ARML questions from 1983 to 1994.]

1989
New York State
Mathematics League
Solutions

Power Question

I. (n, S_n): $(1,1), (2,3), (3,5), (4,8), (5,10), (6,14), (7,16)$

II.   A.   If $a \nmid n$, then the greatest multiple of a that is less than n is also less than or equal to $n - 1$. Thus $[\frac{n}{a}] = [\frac{n-1}{a}]$. If $a \mid n$, let $n = ka$. Then $ka > n - 1 = ka - 1 \geq ka - a$, so $k - 1 \leq \frac{n-1}{a} < k$, and $[\frac{n-1}{a}] = k - 1 = [\frac{n}{a}] - 1$.

      B.   Compare S_n with S_{n-1}, term by term (the final term of S_n can be compared with $[\frac{n-1}{n}]$, which equals 0). For each denominator in S_n that divides n, that term is 1 more than the corresponding term of S_{n-1}. Thus S_n exceeds S_{n-1} by $\tau(n)$.

      C.   We have $S_1 = 1, S_2 \geq S_1 + 2, S_3 \geq S_2 + 2, \ldots, S_n \geq S_{n-1} + 2$. Adding these inequalities produces $S_1 + S_2 + S_3 + \cdots + S_n \geq 1 + S_1 + S_2 + S_3 + \cdots + S_{n-1} + 2(n-1)$, so $S_n \geq 1 + 2(n-1) = 2n - 1$. Note that this holds for $n = 1$ also.

      D.   1.   Clearly, $\tau(n) = 2$ if and only if n is a prime, so n is prime if and only if $S_n = S_{n-1} + 2$.

           2.   The number $\tau(n)$ is odd if and only if n is a perfect square (this is well known, based on the fact that *different* divisors of n can be paired off, except for the square root of a perfect square), so n is a perfect square if and only if S_n has the opposite parity of S_{n-1}.

III. A. Since $2^a - 1 = 2^0 + 2^1 + 2^2 + \cdots + 2^{a-1}$, grouping the terms
          of H_n as in the example shown would produce a sets of
          parentheses, each less than or equal to 1. Thus $H_n \leq a$.

      B. Note that $\frac{n}{a} - 1 < [\frac{n}{a}] \leq \frac{n}{a}$. Then

$$\left(\frac{n}{1} - 1\right) + \left(\frac{n}{2} - 1\right) + \cdots + \left(\frac{n}{n} - 1\right)$$
$$< \left[\frac{n}{1}\right] + \left[\frac{n}{2}\right] + \cdots + \left[\frac{n}{n}\right] \leq \frac{n}{1} + \frac{n}{2} + \cdots + \frac{n}{n},$$

          so $n(1 + \frac{1}{2} + \cdots + \frac{1}{n}) - n < S_n \leq n(1 + \frac{1}{2} + \cdots + \frac{1}{n})$, and
          $n(H_n - 1) < S_n \leq n \cdot H_n$. Note: for $n \geq 3$, only the strict
          inequality signs are needed.

      C. We have

$$S_{1000} \leq 1000 \cdot H_{1000} < 1000 \cdot H_{1023} \leq 1000 \cdot 10 = 10,000.$$

          This topic has great potential for development.

Team Questions

T1. Factoring produces $n^2[(n - 2)(n - 1)(n)(n + 1)(n + 2)]$. The
     product of any five consecutive integers is divisible by 5;
     the product of any four consecutive integers is divisible by 8; the
     products $(n-2)(n-1)(n)$ and $(n)(n+1)(n+2)$ must each be di-
     visible by 3. Thus this product must be divisible by $5 \cdot 8 \cdot 9 = 360$.
     [Checking the greatest common divisor for $n = 3$ and $n = 4$
     shows that no larger divisor works.]

T2. The limit concept implies that eventually the successive terms
     are virtually equal. If a/b is a term of the sequence, setting
     $a/b = (a + 2b)/(a + b)$ produces $a^2 = 2b^2$, so $a/b = \sqrt{2}$. [This
     intuitive approach can be replaced by a rigorous proof involving
     limits.]

T3. The intersection points must lie on the sum of the two equa-
     tions, $5x^2 + 5y^2 = 35$. The area of this circle is 7π.

T4. Note that when a 2-digit number (e.g. 38) is decreased by 9, the
     digital sum does not change, unless the result is a multiple of

10. This will lead to $k = 9$ and $n < 90$. Also, $n - 2k$ must be a multiple of 10, so try $n = 28, 38, \ldots, 88$. Only 88 changes digital sum when $2k$ is added.

T5. *Method* 1: There is no loss of generality if we let the altitude be 1; then the hypotenuse is 4, the median to the hypotenuse is 2, and the distance between the feet of the altitude and median will be $\sqrt{3}$. Since each half of the hypotenuse is 2, we have $p/q = (2 - \sqrt{3})/(2 + \sqrt{3}) = 7 - 4\sqrt{3}$, so $(a, b) = (7, 4)$.

Method 2: Altitude $= \sqrt{pq} = (p + q)/4$. Squaring both sides, clearing fractions and simplifying, then dividing through by q^2, produces a quadratic in p/q. Replacing p/q by x produces

$$x^2 - 14x + 1 = 0,$$

so $x = 7 - 4\sqrt{3}$.

T6. Calling the radii p, q, and s, the sides of $\triangle ABC$ are $s + q, s + p$, and $q + p$. These are in the same ratio as the sines of the angles, namely 2:3:4 respectively. We could now solve $s + q = 2k$, $s + p = 3k, q + p = 4k$ to get the ratio of

$$p : q : s = 5 : 3 : 1$$

leading to the solution (5,3,1). Or we could note that adding two sides of the triangle and subtracting the third produces, for example, $(s + p) + (q + p) - (s + q) = 2p$, so p is 1/2 this expression; this approach leads to

$$p : q : s = (3 + 4 - 2) : (2 + 4 - 3) : (2 + 3 - 4) = 5 : 3 : 1.$$

T7. The equation $z^7 = 1$ implies $z^6 + z^5 + \cdots + z + 1 = 0$. Dividing by z^3 produces

$$f(z) = z^3 + z^2 + z + 1 + \frac{1}{z} + \frac{1}{z^2} + \frac{1}{z^3} = 0.$$

Call the expression to be evaluated $g(z)$, and note that since $z^7 = 1$, then $z^{28} = 1$ and $z^{49} = 1$. Then

$$g(z) = z^3 + \frac{1}{z^3} + z^2 + \frac{1}{z^2} + z + \frac{1}{z} = f(z) - 1 = -1.$$

T8. Note that the first row will contain the integers from 1 through n, the second row contains the integers from $n + 1$ through $2n$, the third row from $2n + 1$ through $3n, \ldots$, and the last row from $(n - 1)n + 1$ through $n \cdot n$. We must end up choosing the integers $a_1 n + b_1, a_2 n + b_2, \ldots, a_n n + b_n$, where the a_i are all different and come from the set $\{0, 1, 2, \ldots, n-1\}$ and the b_i are all different and come from the set $\{1, 2, 3, \ldots, n\}$. The sum will then be $\frac{(n-1)n}{2} \cdot n + \frac{n(n+1)}{2} = \frac{n^3}{2} + \frac{n}{2}$ or $\frac{1}{2}n^3 + \frac{1}{2}n$ or $n(n^2 + 1)/2$.

T9. We use $\varnothing$ to represent the null set. Now the first set of (large) brackets becomes

$$(B \cap C) \cup [(A \cap E) \cap A'] = (B \cap C) \cup \varnothing = (B \cap C).$$

The second set of (large) brackets becomes

$$(C \cap D') \cup [(A \cap E') \cap A'] = (C \cap D') \cup \varnothing = (C \cap D').$$

We then have

$$(B \cap C) \cup (C \cap D') \cup (B' \cup C)' \cup (C \cup D)'$$
$$= (B \cap C) \cup (C \cap D') \cup (B \cap C') \cup (C' \cap D')$$
$$= [(C \cap B) \cup (C \cap D')] \cup [(C' \cap B) \cup (C' \cap D')]$$
$$= [C \cap (B \cup D')] \cup [C' \cap (B \cup D')]$$
$$= (B \cup D') \cap (C \cup C')$$
$$= (B \cup D') \cap I$$
$$= B \cup D'.$$

The answer is (B, D). The main purpose of this problem was to test students' ability to apply the laws of set theory. Using fewer than five sets would have allowed easy solution by use of Venn diagrams.

T10. Let us use the abbreviations s_i for $\sin i$, and c_i for $\cos i$. Then

$$s_1 s_3 s_5 \cdots s_{89} = \frac{(s_1 s_3 \cdots s_{89})(s_2 s_4 s_6 \cdots s_{88})}{s_2 s_4 s_6 \cdots s_{88}}$$
$$= \frac{(s_1 s_{89})(s_2 s_{88}) \cdots (s_{44} s_{46}) s_{45}}{s_2 s_4 \cdots s_{88}}$$

$$= \frac{(s_1 c_1)(s_2 c_2) \cdots (s_{44} c_{44}) s_{45}}{s_2 s_4 \cdots s_{88}}$$

$$= \frac{\frac{s_2}{2} \cdot \frac{s_4}{2} \cdot \frac{s_6}{2} \cdots \frac{s_{88}}{2} \cdot \frac{1}{\sqrt{2}}}{s_2 s_4 s_6 \cdots s_{88}}$$

$$= \left(\frac{1}{2}\right)^{44} \left(\frac{1}{2}\right)^{\frac{1}{2}} = \frac{1}{2^{89/2}},$$

so $n = \frac{89}{2}$ or $44\frac{1}{2}$ or 44.5.

Individual Questions

I1.   Since angle OSP is a right angle, "radius" $\overline{OS}$ is perpendicular to $\overline{PQ}$. Thus it bisects $\overline{PQ}$, so $PS = 6$. The length of $\overline{OP}$ is immaterial!

I2.   Factoring produces $(x - 10)(x)(4x - 1) = 3 \cdot 3 \cdot 13 \cdot 17$. Setting the smallest factor equal to 3 produces $x = 13$ (and the third factor becomes 51). Other possibilities for the smallest factor do not work.

I3.   A consideration of tangent segments to the circle establishes the (fairly well-known) theorem that when a quadrilateral is circumscribed about a circle, the sum of the lengths of one pair of opposite sides must equal the sum of the lengths of the other pair. For the fourth side to be as small as possible, let two opposite sides have lengths 17 and 18. The fourth side has length 14.

I4.   Adding the equations produces $x + y + z = 0$. Squaring both sides gives $x^2 + y^2 + z^2 + 2(xy + xz + yz) = 0$, so the answer is -2.

I5.   The alternate terms are each one less than 3, 6, 12, 24, 48, ... The 50th term of this sequence is $3(2)^{49}$, so the answer is 49.

I6.   Replacing $\tan 4x$ by $(\sin 4x)/(\cos 4x)$, cross-multiplying, and rearranging terms leads to

$$\sin 4x \cos x + \cos 4x \sin x = \cos 4x \cos x - \sin 4x \sin x,$$

so $\sin(4x + x) = \cos(4x + x)$; thus $\tan 5x = 1$, so $5x = 45°$, whereupon $x = 9°$ or 9.

Alternate solution: Dividing each term on the right side by $\cos x$, we recognize the result as $\tan(45° - x)$. Then $4x = 45 - x$ leads to $x = 9$.

I7.   Since this transformation preserves distances (e.g. between the center of the original circle and each point on the circle), the new curve is still a circle, but with center $(8,2)$. Its equation is $(x - 8)^2 + (y - 2)^2 = 25$. Multiplying out shows that $(a, b, c, d) = (1, -16, -4, 43)$.

I8.   Although several different diagrams are possible, in each case it will be found that $\sin \angle CDE = |\cos \angle CDA|$. The side of each rhombus is $\sqrt{29}$. Applying the Law of Cosines to triangle CDA produces $|\cos \angle CDA| = 21/29$. Then the area of rhombus $CDEF$ is $\sqrt{29} \cdot \sqrt{29} \cdot (\sin \angle CDE) = 21$.

Relay #1

R1-1. Try $n = 1, 2, 3, \ldots$ to see if $2608n$ has n digits. Clearly only $n = 5$ works. Therefore, $K = 13040$.

R1-2. We have $S = 8$ and $T = 3$. In base 1,988, this is $(11)^T = 1331$, so the answer is 8.

R1-3. We have $R = 8$ and $T = 35$. The probability is $1/\binom{7}{k}$ so $\binom{7}{k} = 35$. Pascal's Triangle shows $k = 3$.

R1-4. We have $T = 3$ and $k = 5$. Since the median is half the hypotenuse, it creates an isosceles triangle whose angles are θ, θ, and $90 - (\theta/k)$. Setting their sum equal to 180 produces $\theta = 90k/(2k - 1) = 50$.

R1-5. We have $T = 50$ and $P = 6$. Let n equal the number of bills. Then $n = P + \frac{n}{6} + \frac{kn}{5}$. This leads to $n = 30P/(25 - 6k) = 180/(25 - 6k)$. Only $k = 4$ produces a valid n, so $n = 180$.

Relay #2

R2-1. The 4-digit number equals $1001A + 110B = 7(143A + 15B) + 5B$, so $5B$ must be a multiple of 7. Thus $B = 7$, and $A = 9$ produces the maximum of $A + B = 16$.

R2-2. We have $T = 16$ and $k = 4$. The slope equals the tangent of the angle, so $4\sqrt{3}/(p - k) = \sqrt{3}$, producing $p - k = 4$. Consequently, $p = 8$.

R2-3. We have $a = 8$. Whether point B is in quadrant II or IV, the triangle must be a right triangle, with $\overline{AB}$ parallel to an axis. The height (altitude to the hypotenuse) will then be a and the base AB will be $2a$, so the area is $a^2 = 64$.

R2-4. We have $T = 64$ and $K = 16$. The cost is \$1 per mile. The car went K miles in $1/3$ hour, so the average rate was $3K = 48$ mph.

R2-5. We have $T = 48$ and $k = 8$. The first two transformations carry the original (x, y) to $(kx + 2k, ky + 3k)$. The other two carry (x, y) to $(kx + c, ky + d)$. Thus $(c, d) = (2k, 3k) = (16, 24)$.

1990
New York State
Mathematics League
Solutions

Power Question

I.   A. 1. $k = (2n)^2$
        2. $k = (2n + 1)^2$
        3. $k = (2n - 1)(2n)$
        4. $k = (2n)(2n + 1)$

     B. 1. $(-5, -5)$
        2. $(7, 8)$
        3. $(-10, 10)$
        4. $(10, -10)$

     C. 1. Since $(31)(32) < 1000 < (32)(32)$, we see that P_{1000} is between $(-16, 16)$ and $(-16, -16)$. Since $(31)(32) = 992, P_{1000}$ is 8 units below $(-16, 16)$, so is at $(-16, 8)$.
        2. The point $(10, -20)$ is between the points $(-20, -20)$ and $(20, -20)$. Therefore P_k is 30 units to the right of P_{1600}, so we have $k = 1630$.

II. A. The point $(-n^2, n^2)$ is $P_{(2n^2-1)(2n^2)}$. The required points on the parabola are $[-n + n^2]$ units and $[n + n^2]$ units "before" that point (as the spiral develops), so they are the points $P_{(2n^2-1)(2n^2)-(-n+n^2)}$ and $P_{(2n^2-1)(2n^2)-(n+n^2)}$, or $P_{4n^4-3n^2\pm n}$. Thus $(a, b) = (4, -3)$. [Note that for $n = 1$ we get P_0 and P_2, but the formula will not produce P_8! Can you find the logic behind this?]

145

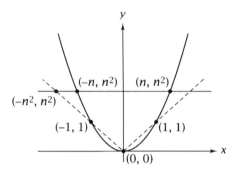

B. The points on the axes would be $P_{4n^2 \pm 2n \pm n} \equiv P_{n(4n \pm 1)}$ or $P_{n(4n \pm 3)}$. The subscripts can only be prime if $n = 1$, and this only produces P_3, P_5, and P_7.

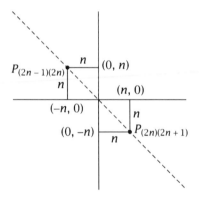

C. [For the cases, refer to the part of the spiral shown below.] Since *successive* points are 1 unit apart, we consider $2k = k + 1$, producing $k = 1$ $[\overline{P_1 P_2}]$. If not successive, the points lie on parallel lines. We consider the four cases:

Case 1. $(2n + 2)^2 + a + 1 = 2[(2n)^2 + a]$, $0 \le a \le 2n$. This yields $n = \frac{2 + \sqrt{9 - a}}{2}$. For the radicand to be an even square, either $a = 5$, so $n = 2$ [but then $a > 2n$] OR $a = 9$, so $n = 1$ [but again $a > 2n$]. Thus there are no acceptable answers.

Case 2. $(2n + 2)(2n + 3) + b + 1 = 2[(2n)(2n + 1) + b]$, $0 \le b \le 2n + 1$. This yields $n = \frac{3 + \sqrt{37 - 4b}}{4}$. For the radicand to be an odd square, $b = 3, 7$, or 9. Finding the corresponding values of n and remembering that b is less than or equal to $2n + 1$, we only get $b = 3, n = 2$. Thus $k = (2n)(2n + 1) + b = 23$. [This is the segment $\overline{P_{23} P_{46}}$.]

Case 3. $(2n + 3)^2 + c + 1 = 2[(2n + 1)^2 + c], 0 \le c \le 2n + 1$. This yields $n = \frac{1+\sqrt{9-c}}{2}$. This only leads to $c = 0, n = 2$ so $k = (2n + 1)^2 + c = 25 \ [\overline{P_{25}P_{50}}]$.

Case 4. $(2n + 3)(2n + 4) + d + 1 = 2[(2n + 1)(2n + 2) + d]$, $0 \le d \le 2n + 2$. This yields $n = \frac{1+\sqrt{37-4d}}{4}$. This leads to no acceptable answers.

Final answer: $\{1, 23, 25\}$.

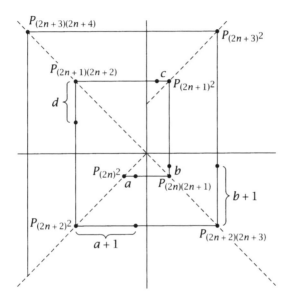

Team Questions

T1. Factoring and simplifying leads to $x + y = 1$. Also, minimum x implies maximum y. Since $y = 1$ implies $x = 0$ (for which $x \not> y$) and $y = \frac{1}{2}$ implies $x = \frac{1}{2}$ ($x \not> y$), we must have $y = 1/3$, so $x = 2/3$.

T2. The true statements are (a) [the perpendicular bisector of every chord passes through the center of the circle], (b) [familiar theorem about chords intersecting within a circle], (c) [these are inscribed angles intercepting the same arc], and (d) [these are opposite angles of inscribed quadrilateral $ABCD$]. The ratio of chord lengths is not, in general, equal to the ratio of their corresponding arcs [e.g. consider (diameter) : (chord equal to radius) = $(\pi r) : (2\pi r/6)$ = 3 : 1, not 2 : 1]. Ans: a, b, c, d (all four required).

T3. From
$$\frac{a}{b} = \frac{\log 9}{\log 16} = \frac{2\log 3}{2\log 4} = \log_4 3$$
we get $4^{a/b} = 4^{\log_4 3} = 3$. Similarly, $3^{b/a} = 4$. The sum is 7.

T4. Note, for example, that 3/5 and 5/3 are only 31 [March] + 30 [April] − 2 = 59 days apart. Our earlier date must be in the first of two consecutive months with 31 days each. A quick check shows that a date in December (its reverse is in February) would be unsatisfactory, so it must be in July. The earlier date is then 7/9, and the answer is (7, 9).

T5. Let CD = x, so AB = $x + 1$. Then $100(x + 1) + x = y^2$, where y is a 2-digit number (since y^2 has four digits). Then $101x = (y + 10)(y - 10)$, and since $y - 10$ has at most two digits, the prime 101 must divide $y + 10$. Since $y + 10 \le 99 + 10 = 109$, we have $y + 10 = 101$ which implies that $y = 91$, so $y^2 = 8281$.

T6. Let $A_n = 1/S_n$. Then $A_1 = A_2 = 1$ and
$$A_n = (S_{n-2} + S_{n-1})/(S_{n-2} \cdot S_{n-1}) = \frac{1}{S_{n-2}} + \frac{1}{S_{n-1}} = A_{n-2} + A_{n-1}$$
for $n > 2$. Thus A_n is a Fibonacci sequence. Then $A_{12} = 144$ and $S_{12} = 1/144$.

T7. *Method 1*: Using long division,

$$
\begin{array}{r}
2^{17} \;+\; 2^{10} \;+\; 2^3 \\[2pt]
2^7 - 1 \;\big)\; \overline{2^{24} \qquad\qquad\qquad\quad +k} \\
2^{24} \;-\; 2^{17} \\ \hline
2^{17} \qquad\qquad +k \\
2^{17} \;-\; 2^{10} \\ \hline
2^{10} \qquad +k \\
2^{10} - 8 \\ \hline
8 \quad +k
\end{array}
$$

For there to be no remainder, k must be 119.

Method 2: Since $2^7 = 128 \equiv 1 \pmod{127}$,

$$2^{24} + k = (2^7)^3 \cdot 2^3 + k \equiv (1)^3 \cdot 8 + k \equiv 8 + k \pmod{127}.$$

If $8 + k \equiv 0$, then $k \equiv -8 \equiv 119(\bmod 127)$.

Method 3: Note that $127 = (2^7 - 1)$ is a factor of $2^8 - 2$, which is a factor of $(2^8 - 2)(2^{16} + 2^9 + 2^2) = 2^{24} - 8$. Therefore 127 is also a factor of $2^{24} - 8 + 127 = 2^{24} + 119$.

T8. Since $\binom{n}{2} = \frac{n(n-1)}{2} = k^2$, the odd factor [$n$ or $(n-1)$] is a positive square, while the even factor is twice a positive square. Set up a table:

odd square less than 100	even factor (= odd factor ±1)	Is even factor 2 times a positive square? If so, compare first two columns; larger number is n
1	2 or 0	yes ; $n = 2$
9	8 or 10	yes ; $n = 9$
25	24 or 26	no
49	48 or 50	yes ; $n = 50$
81	80 or 82	no

The answer is $n = 2, 9, 50$ (all three required)

T9. From triangle BAD, $BD = 25$. Then triangle BCD is also a right triangle. Since angles A and C are supplementary, quadrilateral $ABCD$ is inscriptable in a circle. Applying Ptolemy's Theorem produces $7 \cdot 20 + 15 \cdot 24 = 25 \cdot (AC)$, so $AC = 20$.

T10. Since the triangles cannot agree in three sides, they must agree in two sides and three angles; thus they are similar. If two sides of triangle ABC are a and b, the corresponding sides of triangle DEF are b and b^2/a; thus the third side of triangle ABC is b^2/a, and that of triangle DEF is b^3/a^2. Assume $b > a$ [if $b = a$, the triangles will be congruent]. Also, we need $a \mid b^2$ and $a^2 \mid b^3$. Let $\gcd(a, b) = d$, and $a = da_0, b = db_0$, where $\gcd(a_0, b_0) = 1$. Then $b^2/a = d^2 b_0^2/da_0 = db_0^2/a_0$ and $b^3/a^2 = db_0^3/a_0^2$; clearly we need $a_0^2 \mid d$. [Note: If $a_0 = 1, a = d$, so $b = ab_0$, and the sides of triangle ABC are $a, b_0 a, b_0^2 a$; but then $a + b_0 a > b_0^2 a$, which implies that $1 + b_0 > b_0^2$, so $b_0 = 1$ and $b = a$. Impossible. Therefore we have $b_0 > a_0 > 1$.] Let $d = ka_0^2$, so $b = kb_0 a_0^2$ and $a = ka_0^3$. A check shows that both our triangles will have integer sides, and $k = 1$ produces sides $a_0^3, a_0^2 b_0, a_0 b_0^2$ for triangle ABC

[triangle DEF has sides $a_0^2 b_0, a_0 b_0^2, b_0^3$.] The smallest perimeter occurs when $a_0 = 2$ and $b_0 = 3$, whereupon the perimeter is $8 + 12 + 18 = 38$.

Individual Questions

I1.   Since 15! is a multiple of 9, the sum of its digits $(41 + A)$ must be a multiple of 9. Therefore $A = 4$.

I2.   We have $(a+c)/2 = 10, (a+e)/2 = 7$, and $(c+e)/2 = 8$. Adding the first two equations and subtracting the third produces

$$[(2a + c + e) - (c + e)]/2 = 10 + 7 - 8 = 9,$$

so $a = 9$.

I3.   Since $a + b = a - b$ implies $b = 0$ (clearly prohibited), $a + b \neq a - b$. Then $ab = a/b$, which leads to $a = 0$ or $b = \pm 1$. But $a = 0$ implies $ab = 0$ which implies $a + b$ or $a - b = 0$ (since three are equal). This would imply $b = 0$, which is prohibited. Therefore $b = \pm 1$. Now $b = 1$ implies $a + 1 = a$ or $a - 1 = a$ (both impossible). Therefore $b = -1$. This gives the two possibilities $a - 1 = -a$ and $a + 1 = -a$, leading to $a = 1/2$ or $a = -1/2$. Final answer: $(1/2, -1)$ and $(-1/2, -1)$ [both required].

I4.   Let the line cross $\overline{BC}$ at $P(3,0)$ and $\overline{AB}$ at Q. Draw a perpendicular from Q to $\overline{BC}$, meeting $\overline{BC}$ at R, and let $QR = h$ and $PR = d$. Since $PB = 9, 9h = \frac{1}{2}(6 \cdot 12)$, and $h = 4$. Since $h/(9 - d) = 6/12$, we have $d = 1$. The slope is $h/d = 4$.

I5.   Since $y = \sin 70°$ crosses the sine curve at (for example) $70°$, $110°, 430°, 500°, \ldots$, we have $p : q = 40 : 320 = 1 : 8$. Answer: $(1,8)$. The line $y = \sin \theta$ will be cut in the ratio $(90 - \theta) : (90 + \theta)$; thus for $\theta = 80°$, the ratio is $1:17$, and for $\theta = 89°$, the ratio is $1:179$. There are interesting theorems (and alternate proofs) hidden here.

I6.   [Note that in triangle ABC, AC cannot be 12.] Applying the Law of Cosines to triangle ABD produces $\cos \angle BAD = 1/12$. Since angle ABC is the supplement of angle BAD, cos $\angle ABC = -1/12$. The Law of Cosines applied to $\triangle ABC$ now produces $y = \sqrt{14}$. An alternate approach involves dropping altitudes from B and C, and using the Pythagorean Theorem on several right triangles formed (along with solving some simultaneous equations).

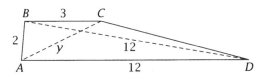

I7.   When a graph is reflected in the line $y = k$, each original y value is replaced by $2k - y$. This concept leads to the final equation $(2 \cdot 3 - y) = (2 \cdot 2 - x)^2$, or $y = -x^2 + 8x - 10$. Ans: $(8,-10)$.

I8.   Each bracket factors beautifully, leading to

$$N = a!b!(a + 2)^2(b + 2)^2$$

$$= (a!)^2[b(b - 1)(b - 2) \cdots (a + 1)](a + 2)^2(b + 2)^2.$$

Thus the expression in brackets here must be a square, which is only possible (according to the "note") if it consists of a single term, b (which itself would have to be a square). Thus $b = a + 1$, and b is a square between 20 and 40. Then $b = 25$ or 36, and $a = 24$ or 35, both required. Note: It has been proven that the product of n consecutive integers cannot equal p^q for integers n, p, and q greater than 1.]

Relay #1

R1-1. If the number is AB, then $(A + B)^2 - (A^2 + B^2) = 2AB = k^2$. Let $A = 9$ and $B = 8$. Answer: 98.

R1-2. We have $T = 98$ and $R = 2$. Clearly areas I, II, III, and IV are all equal, so the original enclosed area is equal to that of rectangle $ACFE = 2R^2 = 8$.

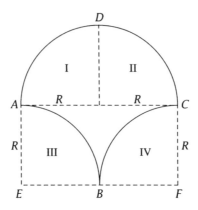

R1-3. We have $A = 8$. From $7 | [100(A-C)+(C-A)]$ we get $7 | 99(A-C)$, which implies that $7 | (A - C)$, so $C = A \pm 7$ and so $C = 1$.

Relay #2

R2-1. If we let that segment of length 4 be the diagonal of the square, we produce a square of smallest area. Area $= \frac{1}{2}$ (diagonal)$^2 = 8$.

R2-2. We have $T = 8$ and $K = 3$. A couple of guesses (e.g. $n = 12$ and $n = 8$) will quickly lead to the (almost certain) conclusion that n must be a power of 2. The largest 3-digit power of 2 is 512. Here is a proof of that conclusion: Let $n = 2^k a$, where a is odd and greater than or equal to 1. If $a > 1, 2^k < n$; then since $2^k | n, 2^k | n/2$ also. Therefore $2^k | 2^{k-1} a$ which implies that $2 | a$. Since this is impossible, $a = 1$ and $n = 2^k$. [Note: If all the "proper" divisors of n also divide $n/3$, then n must be a power of 3.]

R2-3. We have $N = 512$ and $K = 8$. Since the difference in the degree measures of the arcs must be $2(30°)$, and since $60°$ corresponds to an arc length of $2\pi r/6$, we have $K\pi - 2\pi = 2\pi r/6$, which implies that $r = 3K - 6 = 18$.

1991
New York State
Mathematics League
Solutions

Power Question

I.   (a)   We have $3 = 1 + 2$ and $3 = 3$ so $T(3) = 2$; $7 = 3 + 4$, $7 = 7$ so $T(7) = 2$.

           (b)   We have $21 = 1+2+3+4+5+6$, $21 = 6+7+8$, $21 = 10+11$, $21 = 21$ so $T(21) = 4$; $42 = 3 + 4 + 5 + 6 + 7 + 8 + 9$, $42 = 9 + 10 + 11 + 12$, $42 = 13 + 14 + 15$, $42 = 42$ so $T(42) = 4$.

           (c)   We have $9 = 2 + 3 + 4$, $9 = 4 + 5$, $9 = 9$ so $T(9) = 3$; $27 = 2 + 3 + 4 + 5 + 6 + 7$, $27 = 8 + 9 + 10$, $27 = 13 + 14$, $27 = 27$ so $T(27) = 4$.

II.   (a)   The equation $(n)+(n + 1)+(n + 2) = 3n + 3 = 3(n + 1)$ implies $n + 1 = 3x^2$. For $x = 1, 2, 3$ we have $3(n + 1) = 9x^2 = 9, 36, 81$.

           (b)   We have $(n)+(n+1)+ \cdots + (n+7) = 8n+28 = 4(2n+7)$. An even cube must be a multiple of 8, but 2 doesn't divide $(2n + 7)$.

           (c)   We have $(n)+(n+1)+ \cdots +(n+k-1) = kn+(k-1)(k)/2 = k[n + (k - 1)/2]$. This is an integer multiple of k if and only if 2 divides $(k - 1)$, which implies k is odd. Answer: all odd integers greater than 1.

III.   (a)   Since $p = p$, and $p = 2x + 1 = (x)+(x + 1)$, $T(p)$ is at least 2. Let

$$p = (n)+(n + 1)+ \cdots + (n + k - 1)= kn + (k - 1)(k)/2,$$

with k greater than 2. If k is odd ($k = 2y + 1$, with y greater than or equal to 1), $p = (2y + 1)(n)+y(2y + 1)= (2y + 1)(n + y)$; impossible. If k is even ($k = 2z$, with z greater than 1), $p = 2zn + (2z - 1)(z)= z(2n + 2z - 1)$; impossible. Therefore $T(p)= 2$.

      (b)   Since $2^a = 2^a$, $T(2^a)$ is at least 1. If $2^a = kn+(k-1)(k)/2$, k greater than 1, then $k(2n + k - 1)= 2^{a+1}$. Each factor must be a power of two, with k the smaller power. But the factors are of opposite parity. The only odd power of 2 is $2^0 = 1$, so $k = 1$; impossible. Therefore $T(2^a)= 1$.

      (c)   If $p^a = kn + (k - 1)(k)/2$, then $k(2n + k - 1)= 2p^a$. We can factor p^a into two parts in $a + 1$ ways [$1 \cdot p^a, p \cdot p^{a-1}$, $p^2 \cdot p^{a-2},\ldots,p^a \cdot 1$]; multiplying each left factor by 2 produces all possible factorizations of $2p^a$, namely $2 \cdot p^a$, $2p \cdot p^{a-1}, 2p^2 \cdot p^{a-2},\ldots,2p^a \cdot 1$. Now setting k equal to the smaller factor and $(2n + k - 1)$ equal to the larger factor in each case [note that the factors are of opposite parity], we get all possible solutions. Thus $T(p^a)= a + 1$.

      (d)   Following the pattern in III(c), we have $k(2n + k - 1)= 2p^a q^b$. We can factor $p^a q^b$ into two parts in $(a+1)(b+1)$ ways [each factor has the form $p^x q^y$, where x and y are integers and x goes from 0 to a while y goes from 0 to b; thus there are $a + 1$ choices for p^x and $b + 1$ choices for q^y, so we have $(a + 1)(b + 1)$ choices for $p^x q^y$]; we now multiply each left factor by 2, etc. Thus $T(p^a q^b)= (a + 1)(b + 1)= T(p^a) \cdot T(q^b)$.

IV.   (a)   We have $T(15!)= T(2^{11} \cdot 3^6 \cdot 5^3 \cdot 7^2 \cdot 11 \cdot 13)$ = by the "Note" in part III $(1)(7)(4)(3)(2)(2)= 336$.

      (b)   If $N = p^a \cdot q^b \cdot r^c \cdots$, we have

$$12 = (a + 1)(b + 1)(c + 1)\cdots.$$

We consider $12 = 3 \cdot 2 \cdot 2 = 4 \cdot 3 = 6 \cdot 2 = 12 \cdot 1$; using the larger factors with the smaller primes (excluding the prime 2), and remembering to subtract 1 from each factor, we compare $3^2 \cdot 5^1 \cdot 7^1$ with $3^3 \cdot 5^2$ with $3^5 \cdot 5^1$ with 3^{11}. The smallest product is $N = 315$.

(c) We have $k(2n + k - 1) = 2N = 1020$. We want two factors, as close as possible (of *opposite parity*, with k the smaller). Since $1020 = 4 \cdot 3 \cdot 5 \cdot 17$, we quickly find $20 \cdot 51$, so $k = 20$ and $2n + k - 1 = 2n + 19 = 51$ implies $n = 16$.

Team Questions

T1. The circle has center $(5, 7)$ and radius $\sqrt{13}$, so its equation is $(x - 5)^2 + (y - 7)^2 = 13$, leading to $x^2 + y^2 - 10x - 14y + 61 = 0$. Thus the answer is $(10, 14, 61)$.

T2. The angles of regular polygons are $60, 90, 108, 120, \ldots$. The given information implies that the polygons involved are either a triangle and a hexagon, or two squares. Since the sides are integers, the perimeter of 15 can only be for the triangle, each side of which is then 5. The perimeter of the hexagon is 30.

T3. The respective charges are 60¢ per 3/5 mile and 60¢ per 4 minutes. Equivalence implies a rate of 3/5 mile per 4 minutes, or 9 mph.

T4. The projections onto the x-axis of each segment traveled have lengths $\cos^2 1°, \cos^2 2°, \ldots, \cos^2 90°$, so the final x-coordinate is the sum of these, which equals $(\cos^2 1° + \sin^2 1°) + (\cos^2 2° + \sin^2 2°) + \cdots + (\cos^2 44° + \sin^2 44°) + \cos^2 45° = 44\frac{1}{2}$ or 44.5 or $89/2$.

T5. *Method 1*: From Pascal's Triangle, the sum on the left equals $\binom{1992}{992}$, which equals $\binom{1992}{1000}$, so $x = 1000$.

Method 2: We have

$$\frac{1991!}{991!1000!} + \frac{1991!}{992!999!} = \frac{1991!(992 + 1000)}{1000!992!}$$

$$= \frac{1992!}{1000!992!} = \binom{1992}{1000},$$

so $x = 1000$.

T6.   The number 3 can only map to 1 or 5. If 3 maps to 1, then 4
      must map to 2 and 5 must map to 3, thus violating restriction
      #2. Therefore 3 maps to 5. The full mapping is 1 to 3, 2 to 4, 3
      to 5, 4 to 1, 5 to 2.

T7.   There are nine choices for the first digit (since 0 must be ex-
      cluded), and ten choices for each of the following six digits;
      the final seven digits must match the first seven. There are ten
      choices for the central digit. Thus there are $9 \cdot 10^6 \cdot 10$ palin-
      dromes out of the $9 \cdot 10^{14}$ integers in set S. The quotient is
      $1/10^7$, so $k = 7$.

T8.   [Start the diagram with the perpendicular tangents!]
      We have $d^2 = (R + r)^2 + (R - r)^2 = 2(R^2 + r^2) = 2(49 + 1) = 100$,
      so $d = 10$.

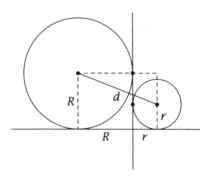

T9.   The first equation is $\sqrt{(x - 3)^2 + y^2} = 2\sqrt{(x + 3)^2 + y^2}$, leading
      to $x^2 + y^2 + 10x + 9 = 0$, or $(x + 5)^2 + y^2 = 16$. The second
      equation is $\sqrt{x^2 + y^2} = k$, or $x^2 + y^2 = k^2$. A sketch of these
      circles shows them to be tangent when $k = 1$ or 9. Only $k = 1$
      is acceptable.

T10. Let angle $BAC = \theta$ and angle $PAQ = \phi$. Since $h/c = \cos(\theta/2) =$
      $\sqrt{[1 + (1/3)]/2} = \sqrt{2/3}$, so $c^2 = 3h^2/2$. From $h^2 + 9 = c^2 =$
      $3h^2/2$, we get $h^2 = 18$ and $(AP)^2 = 19$. Thus $\cos \phi =$
      $1 - 2\sin^2(\phi/2) = 1 - 2(1/19) = 17/19$.

      The problem can also be solved by several applications of the
      Law of Cosines. In general,

$$\cos \phi = \frac{4 + 5 \cos \theta}{5 + 4 \cos \theta}.$$

Note: for $\theta = 90°$, ϕ is about $37°$; for $\theta = 120°$, $\phi = 60°$. This also shows that trisecting the base of an isosceles triangle does *not* trisect the vertex angle. If trisectors of the vertex angle are drawn (instead of base trisectors), then

$$\frac{\text{length of central segment}}{\text{length of entire base}} = \frac{2 \cos(\theta/3) - 1}{2 \cos(\theta/3) + 1}.$$

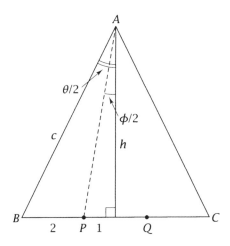

Individual Questions

I1.   Since the product is divisible by 5 and 2, but not by 4, two factors must be 15 and 14 (eliminating 28 and 36). The product is divisible by 9, producing the factor 27. Dividing these factors out leaves 377; this is not a multiple of 3 or 11, so 51 and 11 are eliminated. The only remaining pair whose product ends in a 7 is 13 and 29 (and their product is 377). The sum of these five factors is 98.

I2.   We have $d = r + s = -b$, so $b + d = 0$, and $e = rs = 9$. The roots of $f(x) + g(x) = 2x^2 + (b + d)x + (9 + e) = 2x^2 + 18 = 0$ are $\pm 3i$.

I3.   The correct sum is $10+11+\cdots+99 = (99)(100)/2-(9)(10)/2 =$
      4905. John's palindrome must have been 4,884, so the omitted
      number was 21.

I4.   The equation $133(n-1)+x = 180(n-2)$ implies $x = 47n-227$.
      Since x is between 0 and 180, we can only have $n = 5,6,7,8$
      producing $x = 8,55,102,149$.

I5.   *Method 1*: Area of parallelogram $= 7x = 4(20 - x)$, so $x =$
      $80/11$, and $\sin E = 4/x = 11/20$ or 0.55. Since the sine of each
      angle of the parallelogram is the same, that is also $\sin A$.

      Method 2: We have $x \sin E = 4$ and $(20 - x)\sin E = 7$. Adding
      produces $20 \sin E = 11$, so $\sin E = 11/20$.

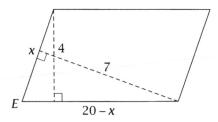

I6.   *Method 1*: The third equation must be a linear combination of
      the first two. If p times the first plus q times the second equals
      the third, then (equating corresponding coefficients) $p+2q = a$,
      $p + 4q = b$, $p + 3q = 2$, and $2p + 5q = 9$. The last two produce
      $p = 17, q = -5$, so $(a,b) = (7,-3)$.

      Method 2: Solve for x (for example) by determinants, but set
      both the numerator and denominator determinants equal to 0
      (no other possibility can imply an infinite number of values for
      x). This produces $b = -3$ and $a + b = 4$, so $(a,b) = (7,-3)$.

      Other approaches to this problem include assigning an arbitrary
      value to x or y, or using Gaussian elimination.

I7.   We have $W^2 = (W/2)^2+(L/2)^2$, so $3W^2 = L^2$, and $L/W = \sqrt{3}$.

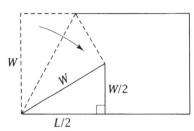

I8.   The highest power of 5 that divides 26! is $[26/5]+[26/5^2]= 6$; the highest power of 2 that divides 26! is $[26/2]+[26/4]+[26/8]$ $+[26/16]= 23$. Thus 26! ends in 6 zeros, and $N(= 26!/10^6)$ is divisible by 2^{17}; therefore the highest power of 4 that divides N is 4^8. The highest power of 3 that divides 26! (and that therefore divides N) is $[26/3]+[26/9]= 10$. Thus the highest power of 12 that divides N is 12^8, so $k = 8$.

Relay #1

R1-1. We have $\sin 2A = 2 \sin A \cos A = 2 \cos B \sin B = \sin 2B = 1/4$.

R1-2. We have $T = 1/4$ and $N = 3$. Multiplying the number of choices for each successive digit gives

$$7 \cdot 8 \cdot 8 \cdot 8 \cdots = 7 \cdot 8^{N-1} = 7 \cdot 8^{12T-1} = 7 \cdot 8^2 = 448.$$

R1-3. We have $T = 448$ and $P = 28$. Using properties of tangents to circles, $GF = 3$ and $EC = 5$. Let $AH = AD = x$ and $BH = BG = y$. Then $2x + 2y + 16 = P$, so $AB = x + y = (P - 16)/2 = [(T/16)-16]/2 = (T - 256)/32 = (T/32)-8 = 6$. Can you show that the minimum possible perimeter for triangle ABC is 25.6?

Relay #2

R2-1. Clearly x is between 3 and 4, so $[x]= 3$. Then $3x = 11$, so $x = 11/3$. Note that (for example) $[x] \cdot x = 12$ has no solutions.

R2-2. We have $T = 11/3$ and $L = 11$. Since each small right triangle is isosceles, the semiperimeter of the rectangle is L. Thus $2L = 6T = 22$. Notice that the perimeter is invariant.

R2-3. We have $T = 22$ and $N = 9$. Since the diagonal of each rectangle is the diameter of the circle, $3^2 + h^2 = N^2 + k^2$. Thus $h^2 - k^2 = N^2 - 9$, so $(h + k)(h - k)= N^2 - 9$, and $h - k = (N^2 - 9)/24 = (81 - 9)/24 = 3$. [The dimensions of the rectangles are $3 \times 13^1/_2$ and $9 \times 10^1/_2$.]

1992
New York State
Mathematics League
Solutions

Power Question

I.   A.   1. $(2, 5)$
         2. D
         3. $T = \sqrt{29}; L = 6$

     B.   1.   We have $T = \sqrt{q^2 + r^2}$ and $L = q + r - 1$.

         2(a).   The parities of the x- and y-coordinates of the final corner will match the parities of q and r, respectively. Thus $(q, r) = $ (odd, even) indicates that the final corner will be $B(1, 0)$; (odd, odd) ends at C; (even, odd) ends at D. No path ends at A since q and r, being relatively prime, cannot both be even.

         2(b).   Since $q + r$ must be even, but they cannot both be even, they must both be odd; thus the final corner will be C.

         2(c).   To end at C, both q and r must be odd (say $q = 2s + 1, r = 2t + 1$); then $T = \sqrt{2(2s^2 + 2t^2 + 2s + 2t + 1)}$; this cannot be rational, as the second factor of the radicand does not contain the factor 2. OR For the length of the path to be rational, q and r must be the lengths of legs of a Pythagorean Right Triangle [integer sides], one of which is always a multiple of

4; but q and r must both be odd for the path to end at C.

3(a). The equation $q + r = 18$ leads to $a = 1/17, 5/13$, or $7/11$ [remembering that q and r are relatively prime].

3(b). The equation $q^2 + r^2 = 65$ is only satisfied by $(q, r) = (1, 8)$ or $(4, 7)$; for the first, $L = 8$ and the path ends at B; for the second, $L = 10$ and the path ends at D.

4(a). Let $q + r = k[= L + 1]$. Then $T^2 = q^2 + r^2 = k^2 - 2qr$; T will be a minimum when T^2 is a minimum, which will occur (since k is constant) when qr is maximum. But since the sum of q and r is constant, their product is maximum when they are as close to one another as possible. This implies that $a[= q/r]$ is as close to 1 as possible, so P_1 is as close to corner C as possible.

4(b1). The equation $q + r = 101$ implies $a = q/r = 50/51$ [since this produces the shortest path]; the final corner is D, and the point on $\overrightarrow{AP_1}$ that corresponds to P_{100} is $J(50, 51)$ [this relates to point J of section IA]. The point corresponding to P_{99} would be the point where $\overline{AJ}$ crosses a grid line, closest to J. The equation of $\overleftrightarrow{AJ}$ is $y = (51/50)x$; since the slope of this line is greater than 1, the point we are seeking is on the grid line $y = 50$ [rather than on $x = 49$], and is between images of B and A. Therefore the image of P_{99} is $(50^2/51, 50)$, which is very close to the image of B. That puts P_{99} at $(1 - [50^2/51 - 49], 0) = (50/51, 0)$. ALTERNATE APPROACH: Since the path has symmetry, $BP_{99} = DP_1 = 50/51$.

4(b2). In general, for all $n < L$, if the image of P_n is (x, y), then $[x] + [y] = n$ (for $n = L, [x] + [y] = x + y = n + 1$). For $n = 22, [x] + [y] = 22$. Then we have either

$$[x] + \left[\left(\frac{51}{50} \right) x \right] = [x] + \left[x + \frac{x}{50} \right] = 22$$

or

$$\left[\left(\frac{50}{51} \right) y \right] + [y] = \left[y - \frac{y}{51} \right] + [y] = 22.$$

Clearly only $x = 11$ works. Then the image of P_{22} is $(11, 51 \cdot 11/50)$, leading to P_{22} being at $(1, 39/50)$.

II.   The images of the corners of the rectangle are of the form $A'(4v, 2w), B'(4v + 2, 2w), C'(4v + 2, 2w + 1)$, and $D'(4v, 2w + 1)$. The lattice points on $\overrightarrow{AP_1}$ are of the form (kq, kr). Let J be the first such point for which kq is even. If q is odd, $k = 2$, and J corresponds to B. If q is "doubly even" [a multiple of 4], then r must be odd, $k = 1$, and J corresponds to D. If q is "singly even" [divisible by 2, but not by 4], then r must be odd, $k = 1$, and J corresponds to C. [Of course, as in section IA, J corresponds to the corner at which the path will end.] No value of q can lead to A as the terminal corner.

III. We have $L = 14, T = 7$, and the final corner is B. A full study of this problem can be done by setting up axes at a $60°$ angle with one another, and tessellating the plane with equilateral triangles. Note which "lattice points" are images of one another. If $CP_1 : P_1B = q : r$, show that $L = 2(q + r - 1), T = \sqrt{q^2 + r^2 + qr}$, and $N \equiv q - r \pmod{3}$ will determine the final corner [$N = 0, 1, 2$ corresponds to corners A, B, C respectively]. Another extension of this problem could involve a ball reflecting off the faces of a cube. And this is but the start!

Team Questions

T1.   Label the lower left vertex A, upper vertex B, other vertex C, altitudes $\overline{AE}$ and $\overline{CD}$.

Method 1: SIMILARITY. From similar triangles ABE and CBD, $2/8 = 3/(2 + x)$, so $x = 10$. [If you prefer a *TRIGONOMETRIC* approach, each of these fractions is cos B.]

Method 2: CIRCLES. A circle with diameter $\overline{AC}$ must pass through D and E. Using a standard theorem about secants [$\overline{BDA}$ and $\overline{BEC}$] to a circle from an outside point, we have $3(8) = 2(2 + x)$, so $x = 10$.

Method 3: PYTHAGOREAN THEOREM. In right triangle ABE, $AE = \sqrt{60}$; thus in right triangle ACE, $AC = \sqrt{60 + x^2}$; then in right triangle ACD, $CD = \sqrt{35 + x^2}$; finally from right triangle BCD, $3^2 + (35 + x^2) = (2 + x)^2$, so $x = 10$.

Method 4: AREA. From right triangles ABE and BCD we get $AE = \sqrt{60}$ and $CD = \sqrt{x^2 + 4x - 5}$. Using these altitudes and the corresponding bases to get the area of triangle ABC leads to $(2 + x)\sqrt{60} = 8\sqrt{x^2 + 4x - 5}$, so $x^2 + 4x - 140 = 0$, producing $x = 10$ as the only positive root.

This simple problem is certainly rich in mathematics.

T2. Let the legs of the triangle be a and $2a$; then the hypotenuse is $a\sqrt{5}$ (and the altitude to the hypotenuse is given as 2). The area $K = (1/2)(2a)(a) = (1/2)(2)(a\sqrt{5})$, so $a = \sqrt{5}$ and $K = 5$.

T3. Factoring, we find that $14! = 2^{11} \cdot 3^5 \cdot 5^2 \cdot 7^2 \cdot 11 \cdot 13$ and that $16! = 2^{15} \cdot 3^6 \cdot 5^3 \cdot 7^2 \cdot 11 \cdot 13$. Thus our answer is the smallest of the numbers $2^{12}, 3^6$, and 5^3. The answer is 125 [or 5^3].

T4. Since $x \cdot y = \mathsf{DDD} = D(111) = D(3 \cdot 37)$, we can have $(x, y) = (3D, 37)$ provided that $D \geq 4$ OR $(x, y) = (3 \cdot \frac{D}{2}, 74)$ if D is 8. There are seven such pairs.

T5. Using the fact that $x^3 + 1 = (x + 1)(x^2 - x + 1)$, we have $9^6 + 1 = (9^2)^3 + 1 = (9^2 + 1)(9^4 - 9^2 + 1) = 82 \cdot 6481 = 2 \cdot 41 \cdot 6481$. From the given information, it must be true that 6,481 is a prime, and that must be the correct answer.

T6. Since AB is a prime, B must be 1,3,7, or 9. There are no squares in the 70's or 90's, so B = 1 or 3 and C = 6. A quick check of the factors of the integers from 61 through 69 shows that only 63 and 68 satisfy the third condition of the problem, so A = 3 or 8. Remembering condition one, the only 4-digit numbers that work are 3,163 and 8,368.

T7. $f(f(x)) = |\,3|3x - 1| - 1\,| = x$ implies $3|3x - 1| - 1 = \pm x$, so $3|3x - 1| = 1 \pm x$. If $x \geq 1/3$, we have $9x - 3 = 1 \pm x$, leading to $x = 1/2$ or $2/5$, both of which check. If $x < 1/3$, we have $3 - 9x = 1 \pm x$, leading to $x = 1/5$ or $1/4$. Answer: 1/4, 1/5, 2/5, 1/2.

T8. *Method 1*: Let $AO = p, BO = q$, and $CO = r$. Then $pq = 8, pr = 12$, and $qr = 24$ quickly produces $p = 2, q = 4, r = 6$ [to see this, note that $(pqr)^2 = 8 \cdot 12 \cdot 24$, so $pqr = 48$; then $p = pqr/qr = 48/24 = 2$, etc.]. The Pythagorean Theorem now gives us the sides of triangle ABC, namely $AB = \sqrt{4+16} = \sqrt{20} = 2\sqrt{5}, AC = 2\sqrt{10}$, and $BC = 2\sqrt{13}$. We now apply Hero's Formula to triangle ABC [Area = $\sqrt{s(s-a)(s-b)(s-c)}$, where $s = \sqrt{5} + \sqrt{10} + \sqrt{13}$]. Careful arithmetic manipulation produces Area $= 14$.

Method 2: It can be shown that if the areas of triangles OAB, OAC, OBC, and ABC are K_1, K_2, K_3, and K, respectively, then $K^2 = K_1^2 + K_2^2 + K_3^2$. Thus $K^2 = 16 + 36 + 144 = 196$, and $K = 14$.

T9. Adding $1 + 2 + 3 + \cdots + n$ to both sides leads to

$$2 \cdot \frac{n(n+1)}{2} = \frac{(n+k)(n+k+1)}{2},$$

so $n^2 - (2k-1)n - k(k+1) = 0$. Then $n = \frac{2k-1+\sqrt{8k^2+1}}{2}$. We need the smallest $k > 1$ that makes $8k^2 + 1$ a perfect square. Trying successive integer values, we shortly reach $k = 6$, whereupon $n = (11 + \sqrt{289})/2 = 14$. [Sample values of (k, n): $(1, 2)$ leads to $1 + 2 = 3$; $(6, 14)$ leads to $1 + 2 + \cdots + 14 = 15 + 16 + \cdots + 20$; $(35, 84)$ leads to $1 + 2 + \cdots + 84 = 85 + 86 + \cdots + 119$; etc. One can find recursive definitions that will produce successive k's and successive n's.]

T10. Let the pentagon be $ABCDE$, with $AE = 6$. Let $AD = a$ and $AC = BD = CE = b$ [the equality of chords comes from the equality of their arcs]. Applying Ptolemy's Theorem to inscribed quadrilateral $ABCD$, we have [1] $16a + 16^2 = b^2$; applying it to quadrilateral $ACDE$, we have [2] $16b + 96 = ab$. Solving [1] for a and substituting into [2] leads to $b^3 - 2^9 b - 2^9 \cdot 3 = 0$. This equation has only one positive root (by Descartes' Law of Signs), and that is $b = 24$ (e.g. use the Rational Roots Theorem). Triangles ABC and CDE are isosceles triangles (sides 16, 16, 24), each with area $48\sqrt{7}$ (easily found by dropping an altitude or by Hero's Formula); triangle ACE is isosceles (sides 24, 24, 6), with area $27\sqrt{7}$. The sum of these gives the pentagon's area, $123\sqrt{7}$, so $k = 123$.

Individual Questions

I1. Remembering our Pythagorean Triples, this is $2(25^2)^5 + 3(25^2)^5 =$
$5 \cdot 25^{10} = 5^{21}$, so $k = 21$.

I2. This is the number of squares *between* $(7^2)^2 [= 49^2]$ and $(2^2)^7$
$[= (2^7)^2 = 128^2]$, which is $128 - 49 - 1 = 78$.

I3. This is $(3^6 - 2^6)^2 = [(3^3 + 2^3)(3^3 - 2^3)]^2 = [35 \cdot 19]^2$. Thus the
answer is 19.

I4. Only one position is possible for the hexagon! Letter the vertices
clockwise (although counterclockwise would do as well), and call
the origin O. Then B is at $(0, 4\sqrt{3})$ and F is at $(12, 0)$. Clearly D
is at $(12, 8\sqrt{3})$.

I5. Let the midpoint of $\overline{AB}$ be M; then crease $\overline{XY}$ will be the perpendicular bisector of $\overline{CM}$. Let P be the intersection of $\overline{XY}$ and $\overline{CM}$.
Then $CP = (1/2)(CM) = (1/2)(1/2)(AB) = 9$, and the area of tri-
angle $XYC = (1/2)(CP)(XY) = 90$. It is interesting to note that
for the crease not to touch or cross the hypotenuse, the larger
acute angle of triangle ABC must be less than $60°$. Furthermore,
$AB/2 \le XY < AB/\sqrt{3}$. Can you prove these results?

I6. We see that $\cos x - \tan x = \sec x - \cos x$ which implies that
$\cos^2 x - \sin x = 1 - \cos^2 x$. Hence, $2\sin^2 x + \sin x - 1 = 0$ which
implies that $\sin x = -1$ or $1/2$. Thus $x = 270°, 30°$, or $150°$
[between $0°$ and $360°$]. Substituting each of these into the terms
of the progression, we find the following: [1] $x = 270°$ makes
the third term undefined. [2] $x = 30°$ produces the sequence
$1/\sqrt{3}[= 2\sqrt{3}/6], \sqrt{3}/2[= 3\sqrt{3}/6], 2/\sqrt{3}[= 4\sqrt{3}/6]$; $\cot 30° =$
$\sqrt{3} = 6\sqrt{3}/6$ would be the 5th term, so $k = 5$. [3] $x = 150°$
produces the sequence $-2\sqrt{3}/6, -3\sqrt{3}/6, -4\sqrt{3}/6$; $\cot 150° =$
$-6\sqrt{3}/6$ is the 5th term in this case also.

I7. *Method 1*: Carefully choosing which factors to multiply, we get

$$[r^2 + 5r - 6][r^2 + 5r + 6] = [(r^2 + 5r + 7) - 13][(r^2 + 5r + 7) - 1]$$
$$= (-13)(-1) = 13.$$

Method 2: Solve the equation and substitute one root into the called for product [takes longer!].

I8.   Connect the centers of the circles, connect each center to the nearest vertex of the triangle, and draw perpendiculars from the centers to the hypotenuse. Label the feet of the perpendiculars *P* and *Q*, and label the vertices of the triangle *C* (at the right angle), *A* (nearer to *P*) and *B* (nearer to *Q*). Let $AP = x$ and $BQ = y$; call each radius *r*, and note that $PQ = 2r$. We will solve this problem for any right triangle, using the theorem that when 2 tangents are drawn to a circle from an outside point, the line joining the center of the circle to that point bisects the angle formed by the tangents. [Of course, using numbers for *a*, *b*, and *c* simplifies the work considerably.] Then

$$r/x = \tan A/2$$
$$= \sqrt{(1 - \cos A)/(1 + \cos A)}$$
$$= \sqrt{(1 - b/c)/(1 + b/c)}$$
$$= \sqrt{(c - b)/(c + b)}$$
$$= \sqrt{(c^2 - b^2)/(c + b)^2}$$
$$= a/(c + b).$$

Similarly, $r/y = \tan B/2 = b/(c + a)$. Then

$$c = x + y + 2r = r(c + b)/a + r(c + a)/b + 2r,$$

so

$$abc = rb(c + b) + ra(c + a) + 2abr.$$

Thus

$$r = abc/(bc + b^2 + ac + a^2 + 2ab)$$
$$= abc/[(a + b)^2 + c(a + b)]$$
$$= abc/[(a + b)(a + b + c)].$$

Nice formula! For our problem, $r = (3 \cdot 4 \cdot 5)/(7 \cdot 12) = 5/7$.

Relay #1

R1-1. This is $\log 2^{16} + \log 5^{16} = 16(\log 2 + \log 5) = 16 \log 10 = 16$.

R1-2. We have $T = 16$ and $D = 8$. The length of the semi-diagonal of the square must be b. The equation of the line containing the side of the square through (1992, D) will be $y = -x + b$. Substituting, $b = y + x = 1992 + D = 2000$.

R1-3. We have $T = 2000$ and $R = 24$. Equating the expressions produces $n^2 + n - 56 = 0$, so $n = 7$ or -8. Then each expression equals $175 - R$ or $160 - R$. For $R = 24$, only the first is a prime, $p = 151$.

Relay #2

R2-1. *Method 1*: Let the centroid of the triangle [intersection of the medians] be $G(4, 2)$, and the vertices be $A(a, 0), B(0, b)$, and $O(0, 0)$. Let two medians be $\overline{AM}$ and $\overline{BN}$. Noting that a vertical line through G would be parallel to $\overline{OM}$, that line would cut $\overline{MA}$ and $\overline{OA}$ proportionally. Since $MG = (1/3)(MA)$, then we have $4 = (1/3)(OA)$, so $OA = a = 12$. Similarly considering a horizontal line through G, we find that $2 = (1/3)(OB)$, so $OB = b = 6$. The area of triangle $OAB = (1/2)ab = 36$.

Method 2: It can be shown that the coordinates of the centroid of any triangle are the "averages" of the coordinates of its vertices [considering abscissas and ordinates separately]. Then $a/3 = 4$ and $b/3 = 2$ imply $a = 12, b = 6$, and the area of this right triangle is $(1/2)ab = 36$.

R2-2. We have $T = 36$ and $R = 9$. Thus $xR/(R + x) = 6$, which implies that $x = 6R/(R - 6) = 18$.

R2-3. We have $T = 18$. Either $x - T = 0$, so $x = T$, or $x - T$ is the leg of a right triangle with integer sides whose other leg is 4. The only such triangle is the 3-4-5 triangle, so $x - T = 3$ and $x = T + 3$. This is larger than T, so $x = T + 3 = 21$.

Tiebreaker Solutions

1. The answer is 41. Nine years after using this as a tiebreaker, we gave it (with slight variation) as question T8 in ARML 1992. Refer to that solution for essential details.

2. Circumscribe a circle about the polygon. Each minor arc is $360°/7$. Angle $APB = \frac{1}{2}\left(\frac{360°}{7} + \frac{3\cdot360°}{7}\right) = \frac{720°}{7}$.

3. An identity is true for all values of the variable. Then $x = 0$ implies $-1 = -A+B-C+D$, and $x = 2$ implies $33 = A+B+C+D$. Adding produces $B + D = 16$.

4. Let $\overline{AC}$ and $\overline{BP}$ intersect at Q, and let $AQ = p$, $CQ = q$, $BQ = t$, and $PQ = x$. Utilizing two "angle-bisector" theorems and one theorem about chords intersecting in a circle, we have (1) $p : q = 6 : 8$ implies $p = 6k$, $q = 8k$. Thus $14k = 7$, so $k = 1/2$. Therefore $p = 3$ and $q = 4$. (2) $t^2 = 6 \cdot 8 - p \cdot q$. Therefore $t^2 = 36$, so $t = 6$. (3) $tx = pq$, so $6x = 12$, making $x = 2$, and thus $BP = 8$.

5. By the A.M.-G.M. Inequality, $(x+4y+16z)/3 \geq \sqrt[3]{(x)(4y)(16z)}$ which implies that $40 \geq 4\sqrt[3]{xyz}$, so $xyz \leq 1000$. Therefore

$$\log x + \log y + \log z = \log xyz \leq \log 1000 = 3.$$

6. Note that $A_n = n^2$ and

$$B_n = \log(A_1 A_2 \cdots A_n) = \log(1^2 \cdot 2^2 \cdots n^2) = 2\log(n!).$$

Then $B_6 + B_7 = B_x$ which implies that $2\log(6!)+2\log(7!) = 2\log(6! \cdot 7!) = 2\log(x!)$, so $x! = 6! \cdot 7! = 10!$ and thus $x = 10$.

7. Note that if $a = 4 - \sqrt{15}$, then $0 < a < 1$. Now let

$$b = (4 + \sqrt{15})^3 + (4 - \sqrt{15})^3.$$

Expanding and simplifying leads to $b = 1208$. Then $(4 + \sqrt{15})^3 = 1208 - a^3$, which is between 1,207 and 1,208. The answer is 1,207.

8. We have $\cos 2x = 2\cos x$ which implies that $2\cos^2 x - 1 = 2\cos x$. Solving this quadratic equation leads to $\cos x = (1 \pm \sqrt{3})/2$. Only $\cos x = (1 - \sqrt{3})/2$ is valid. Then $(\sin 2x)/\sin x = \cos x = 1 - \sqrt{3}$.

9. We have

$$S_n = [1 + 2 + \cdots + n]^2 = \left[\frac{n(n+1)}{2}\right]^2,$$

so $\frac{1}{S_n} = \frac{2}{n(n+1)}$. Then

$$\frac{1}{\sqrt{S_1}} + \frac{1}{\sqrt{S_2}} + \cdots + \frac{1}{\sqrt{S_{1985}}}$$

$$= \frac{2}{1 \cdot 2} + \frac{2}{2 \cdot 3} + \frac{2}{3 \cdot 4} + \cdots + \frac{2}{1985 \cdot 1986}$$

$$= 2\left[\left(\frac{1}{1} - \frac{1}{2}\right) + \left(\frac{1}{2} - \frac{1}{3}\right) + \left(\frac{1}{3} - \frac{1}{4}\right) + \cdots + \left(\frac{1}{1985} - \frac{1}{1986}\right)\right]$$

$$= 2\left[1 - \frac{1}{1986}\right]$$

$$= 2 \cdot \frac{1985}{1986}$$

$$= \frac{1985}{993}.$$

10. Factoring produces $y^2(y - x - 3) = 4x^2(y - x - 3)$. Therefore $(y - x - 3) \cdot (y^2 - 4x^2) = 0$, and so $y - x - 3 = 0$ or $y + 2x = 0$ or $y - 2x = 0$. Thus the graph of the original equation consists of three straight lines. These intersect at $(0,0)$, $(-1, 2)$, and $(3, 6)$. The area of the triangle with these vertices is 6.

11. Note that the shortest altitude goes to the longest side. If the 4 and 5 are the legs of the right triangle, the third altitude goes to the hypotenuse; thus it would be the shortest, and the longest would be 5. If the 4 and 5 are not both legs, then one of them is the altitude to the hypotenuse; it must then be the 4. Now one segment of the hypotenuse is clearly 3, and the other segment (using right triangle relationships) is found to be 16/3.

The missing leg, by the Pythagorean Theorem, is 20/3, and is therefore the longest possible altitude.

12. Completing the three parallelograms, we note that (e.g.) $CP = AB = QC$ and $\overline{CP} \| \overline{AB} \| \overline{QC}$. Thus QCP must be a straight line segment with midpoint C. Then $(a + b)/2 = 6$, so $a + b = 12$. Similarly, $b + c = 2$ and $a + c = 8$. Adding and dividing by 2 produces $a + b + c = 11$. Note that this is the sum of the abscissas of points A, B, and C!

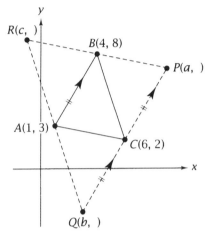

13. The common root r must also be a root of the difference of the two equations, which is $x(b - c) + (c - b) = 0$. Thus $r = 1$. Using the product of the roots, we find that $s = c$ and $t = b$, so $s + t = c + b$. Letting $x = 1$ in either of the original equations produces $1 + b + c = 0$, so $s + t = c + b = -1$.

14. The two lines must be reflections of one another in $y = x$; thus if (a, b) is on one line, then (b, a) is on the other line. This shows that their slopes are reciprocals. Therefore $pq = 1$. [This can also be shown by using the formula for the tangent of the angle between two lines.] Now

$$(p - q)^2 = (p + q)^2 - 4pq = 13 - 4 = 9,$$

so $p - q = 3$.

15. Let $AB = n$ and $PB = q$. Then $(q + n)(q) = 81/4$, which implies $4q^2 + 4qn - 81 = 0$, so $q = \left(-n + \sqrt{n^2 + 81}\right)/2$. We must find all integers n that make $n^2 + 81$ a perfect square, say a^2. Then

$a^2 - n^2 = 81$ yields $(a - n)(a + n) = 1 \cdot 81$ or $3 \cdot 27$ [note that $(a - n)(a + n) = 9 \cdot 9$ implies $n = 0$]. This leads to two pairs of simultaneous equations: $a - n = 1$, $a + n = 81$ and $a - n = 3$, $a + n = 27$. These produce $n = 40$ and 12.

16. We have

$$\left(5^{\log 2 + \log 9}\right)\left(2^{\log 3 + \log 6}\right) = \left(5^{\log 18}\right)\left(2^{\log 18}\right) = 10^{\log 18} = 18.$$

17. [Note that $x = 45°$ does not satisfy the equation.] Multiplying numerator and denominator of the right side by $(\cos x - \sin x)$, we get $\tan 2x = (\cos^2 x - 2 \sin x \cos x + \sin^2 x)/(\cos^2 x - \sin^2 x)$, so $(\sin 2x)/(\cos 2x) = (1 - \sin 2x)/\cos 2x$. Thus $2 \sin 2x = 1$ and $2x = 30°$ or $150°$ which implies that $4x = 60°$ or $300°$, so $\tan 4x = \pm\sqrt{3}$. The answer is $\sqrt{3}$.

18. We have

$$3^{12}(3^2 + 3) - 12 = 12(3^{12} - 1)$$

$$= 12(3^6 + 1)(3^6 - 1)$$

$$= 12(3^6 + 1)(3^3 + 1)(3^3 - 1)$$

$$= 12 \cdot 730 \cdot 28 \cdot 26$$

$$= 12 \cdot 73 \cdot 10 \cdot 28 \cdot 26.$$

Clearly, the largest prime factor is 73.

19. We have $\sqrt{5}^{2\sqrt{2}} \cdot \sqrt[3]{2}^{3\sqrt{2}} = 5^{\sqrt{2}} \cdot 2^{\sqrt{2}} = 10^{\sqrt{2}}$; then $\log 10^{\sqrt{2}} = \sqrt{2}$.

20. Call the origin O, let $OA = 1$, and $OB = m$. Considering altitudes in successive right triangles, we find that $OC = m^2$, $OD = m^3$, and $OE = m^4$. Then $m^4 - 1 = m^2 + 1$, leading to $m^4 - m^2 - 2 = 0$, which implies that $(m^2 - 2)(m^2 + 1) = 0$, so $m = \sqrt{2}$.

21. For a 1-digit number, A, A^3 is always divisible by A; for a 2-digit number, AB, $A^3 + B^3[= (A + B)(A^2 - AB + B^2)]$ is always divisible by $A + B$. Therefore the number has at least three digits. Since the integers from 100 through 110 each contain a zero, this divisibility property is equivalent to that of 2-digit numbers. Therefore try 111 (we get 3 divides 3), then 112 (for which 4 does *not* divide 10). Thus, the answer is 112.

22. [One of many methods] The lattice points will be equally spaced along a line segment from $(0, 70)$ to $(110, 0)$, so their x-coordinates will form an arithmetic sequence. Their average will then be $110/2 = 55$.

23. We have

$$2r^2 + rs + s^2 + r + 7 = [r^2 + r + 7] + [r^2 + rs + s^2]$$
$$= 0 + [(r + s)^2 - rs]$$
$$= (-1)^2 - 7 = -6.$$

24. Call the integers $a - d$, a, and $a + d$. Then

$$[(a - d)^3 + a^3 + (a + d)^3]/[(a - d) + a + (a + d)]$$
$$= [3a^3 + 6ad^2]/3a$$
$$= a^2 + 2d^2 = 81.$$

Clearly a must be odd, but less than 10. Testing $a = 1$ or 5, we get irrational d's. Now $a = 3$ implies $d = \pm 6$, producing a negative term in the progression. Furthermore, $a = 9$ implies $d = 0$, so the terms aren't distinct. Only $a = 7$ works. Since $d = \pm 4$, the terms are 3, 7, 11.

25. One of the many methods

$$m_{OC} = \tan 2\theta = \frac{2 \tan \theta}{1 - \tan^2 \theta} = \frac{3/2}{1 - (9/16)} = \frac{24}{7}.$$

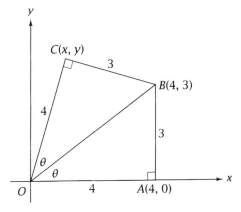

26. Draw a radius (length r) to the tangent point, and let the line make an angle θ with the positive x-axis. Then $\tan \theta = 4/3$ implies $\sin \theta = 4/5 = r/(r + 1)$, so $r = 4$. Thus $b = 2r + 1 = 9$.

27. We need $x^2 + 1 = y^2 + 10000$, $x \geq 1$, $y \geq 1$. Now

$$(x + y)(x - y) = 9999 = 3 \cdot 3 \cdot 11 \cdot 101.$$

Considering different groupings of factors, and noting that $x > y$ and $(x + y) > (x - y)$, we get a series of equations. It is only important to see how many equations there are, rather than solve them, since each must lead to a valid (x, y):

$x + y = 9999$ [uses all 4 factors; $(x - y) = 1$]

$\left. \begin{array}{l} x + y = 3333 \\ x + y = 909 \end{array} \right\}$ [each uses 3 of the factors]

$\left. \begin{array}{l} x + y = 1111 \\ x + y = 303 \end{array} \right\}$ [each uses 2 of the factors]

$x + y = 101$ [uses 1 factor only]

Answer: 6. [e.g. $x + y = 9999$, $x - y = 1$ yields $x = 5000$, $y = 4999$; the common element is 25,000,001]

28. We must have $n = 5k$, $n = 6l + 3 = 3(2l + 1)$ which is 3 times an odd integer, and $n = 7m$. Therefore n is an odd multiple of $5 \cdot 3 \cdot 7[= 105]$. The smallest such n greater than 200 is 315.

29. *Method 1*: Call the product n and note that 9966333 is a multiple of 3. Thus we have $(3k + 1)(3k - 1) = 9k^2 - 1 = n$ which implies that $9k^2 = n + 1$, so $9|(n + 1)$. Therefore $9|99327A93466889$. Thus 9 divides the sum of the digits of $n + 1$, which is $83 +$ A, so A $= 7$.

Method 2: Considering this product modulo 9, we have $1 +$ A $= 2 \cdot 4$, so A $= 7$.

APPENDICES

NYSML Winners

TEAM WINNERS

	(1st, 2nd, 3rd place)
1989	New York City - team A Nassau - team A New York City - teamB [tie for 2nd place]
1990	New York City - team A Westchester - team A New York City - team B
1991	New York City - team A Nassau - Gold team New York City - team B
1992	New York City - team A New York City - team B Monroe - team A

INDIVIDUAL WINNERS

	(1st, 2nd, 3rd place)
1989	Sandy Kutin (Nassau - team A) Sanjoy Dasgupta (New York City - team A) Mike Alexander (Monroe - team A) Josh Newman (New York City - team B) [tie for 3rd place]
1990	Joe Kanapka (Westchester - team A) Tony Wang (New York City - team A) Robert Johnston (New York City - team A)
1991	David Nowakowski (New York City - team A) Brien Oberstein (New York City - team A) Vadim Strizhevsky (New York City -team B)
1992	Stefano Merlo (New York City - team A) Ruth Britto-Pacumio (Southern Tier) Jaime Chang (New York City - team A)

ARML Winners

<table>
<tr><td rowspan="7">TEAM WINNERS</td><td colspan="2">(Division A)   (1st, 2nd, 3rd place)</td></tr>
<tr><td>1989</td><td>Chicago - team A
Ontario - team A
New York City - team A</td></tr>
<tr><td>1990</td><td>Chicago - team A
Ontario - team A
New York City - team A</td></tr>
<tr><td>1991</td><td>Chicago - team A
Ontario - team A
New York City - team A   [tie for 2nd place]</td></tr>
<tr><td>1992</td><td>Georgia - team A
Massachusetts - team A
Upstate New York - team A</td></tr>
<tr><td>1993</td><td>Thomas Jefferson - team A
Chicago - team A
Georgia - team A</td></tr>
<tr><td>1994</td><td>New York City - team A
Massachusetts - team A
Thomas Jefferson - team A</td></tr>
</table>

<table>
<tr><td rowspan="7">INDIVIDUAL WINNERS</td><td colspan="2">(1st, 2nd, 3rd place)</td></tr>
<tr><td>1989</td><td>Sam Vandervalde (Lynchburg/Harrisonburg)
Art DiBianca (North Carolina - team A)
Lenny Ng (North Carolina - team A)</td></tr>
<tr><td>1990</td><td>Akira Negi (North Carolina - team A)
Nick Tallyn (Chicago - team A)
Joshua Fischman (Montgomery - team A)</td></tr>
<tr><td>1991</td><td>Andrew Schultz (Chicago - team A)
Mark Lucianovic (Fairfax - team A)
Stefano Merlo (New York City - team A)</td></tr>
<tr><td>1992</td><td>Robert Kleinberg (Upstate New York)
Paul Li (Massachusetts - team A)
Joshua Faber (Upstate New York)</td></tr>
<tr><td>1993</td><td>Jeremy Bem (Upstate New York)
Lenny Ng (North Carolina - team A)
Steve Wang (Chicago - team A)</td></tr>
<tr><td>1994</td><td>Noam Shazeer (Massachusetts - team A)
Kevin Purbhoo (Ontario - team A)
Andrei Gnepp (Ohio)</td></tr>
</table>

Glossary

π	pi: ratio of the circumference of a circle to its diameter.
$\sum_{i=1}^{n} a_i$	The sum $a_1 + a_2 + \cdots + a_n$.
$\tau(n)$	Number of divisors of the positive integer n.
$\varnothing$	The null set.
$m \times n$	m by n (as in an array with m rows and n columns).
$\angle ABC$	Angle ABC.
$\triangle ABC$	Triangle ABC.
$\triangle ABC \cong \triangle DEF$	Triangles ABC and DEF are congruent.
$\overline{AB}$	Line segment from A to B.
AB	Length of the line segment $\overline{AB}$.
$\overrightarrow{AB}$	Ray from A through B.
$\overleftrightarrow{AB}$	Infinite line through points A and B.
$\overset{\frown}{AB}$	Arc of circle from A to B.
$\angle ABC \overset{\circ}{=} \overset{\frown}{CD}$	equal in degrees.
$\overline{AB} \| \overline{CD}$	$\overline{AB}$ is parallel to $\overline{CD}$.
$\overline{AB} \perp \overline{CD}$	$\overline{AB}$ is perpendicular to $\overline{CD}$
$d \mid n$	d divides n.
$d \nmid n$	d does not divide n.
$\mid x \mid$	Absolute value of real number x: $\mid x \mid = x$ if $x \geq 0$ and $\mid x \mid = -x$ if $x < 0$.
$\mid z \mid$	Modulus of complex number z: If $z = a + bi$ where a and b are real, then $\mid z \mid = \sqrt{a^2 + b^2}$.
(a, b)	An ordered pair: the number a followed by the number b.

$P(a, b)$ Point P with Cartesian coordinates (a, b).

$\binom{n}{k}$ Binomial coefficient: the number of combinations of n things taken k at a time. Sometimes written as $_nC_k$ or C_n^k. We have

$$\binom{n}{k} = \frac{n!}{k!(n-k)!} \quad \text{and} \quad \binom{n}{0} = 1.$$

$x \in A$ x is an element of the set A.

$n!$ n factorial $= 1 \cdot 2 \cdot 3 \cdots (n-1) \cdot n$. By definition, $0! = 1$.

$f: A \to B$ A function f that maps A into B.

$a \equiv b \pmod{p}$ Number-theoretic congruence: $a - b$ is divisible by p.

$[x]$ If a problem states that brackets refer to the Greatest Integer Function, then $[x]$ means the largest integer that is less than or equal to x. Sometimes written as $\lfloor x \rfloor$.

$A \cup B$ The union of sets A and B: all elements in either set.

$A \cap B$ The intersection of sets A and B: all elements in both sets.

A' The complement of the set A.

ABCDE   When this font is used, it means that the letters represent digits of a number written in base 10. The digits are to be juxtaposed rather than multiplied together. Thus, ABC represents the 3-digit number with digits A, B, and C. (On the actual ARML and NYSML exams, these digits were usually underlined.)

A.M.-G.M. inequality   If $a_1, a_2, \ldots, a_n$ are nonnegative real numbers, then their arithmetic mean $\left(\sum_{i=1}^{n} a_i \right) / n$ is no less than their geometric mean $\left(\prod_{i=1}^{n} a_i \right)^{1/n}$, with equality if and only if all these numbers are equal.

arithmetic progression   A sequence $a_1, a_2, \ldots$, with $a_{k+1} - a_k = d$, d the common difference.

ARML   American Regions Mathematics League.

Brahmagupta's Formula	The area of a cyclic quadrilateral with sides of lengths a, b, c, and d is

$$\sqrt{(s-a)(s-b)(s-c)(s-d)}$$

where $s = (a+b+c+d)/2$.

circumcenter	The circumcenter of a triangle is the center of the circumscribed circle.
circumcircle	Circumscribed circle of a triangle.
compute	Find, in simplest form.
convex polygon	A simple polygon all of whose interior angles are less than $180°$.
cyclic points	A set of points that lie on a circle.
cyclic polygon	A polygon that can be inscribed in a circle.
Diophantine equation	An equation that is to be solved for integer values of its variables.
divisor	The integer d is a divisor of n if $d > 0$ and if there is an integer k such that $n = dk$.
F_n	The nth Fibonacci number, defined by $F_0 = 0$, $F_1 = 1$, and $F_n = F_{n-1} + F_{n-2}$, for $n > 1$.
Fibonacci number	A member of the sequence $0, 1, 1, 2, 3, 5, \ldots$, where each number is the sum of the previous two numbers.
$\gcd(m, n)$	The greatest common divisor of integers m and n.
geometric progression	A sequence $a_1, a_2, \ldots$, with $a_{k+1} = ra_k$, r the common ratio.
H_n	Harmonic number: $H_n = \sum_{k=1}^{n} \frac{1}{k}$.
harmonic mean	The harmonic mean of two numbers a and b is $2ab/(a+b)$.
Hero's Formula	The area of a triangle with sides of lengths a, b, and c is

$$\sqrt{s(s-a)(s-b)(s-c)}$$

where $s = (a+b+c)/2$.

Heronian triangle	A triangle with integer sides and integer area.
i	imaginary unit: $i = \sqrt{-1}$.

incenter   The center of the inscribed circle of a triangle.

incircle   The inscribed circle of a triangle.

L_n The nth Lucas number, defined by $L_0 = 2$, $L_1 = 1$, and $L_n = L_{n-1} + L_{n-2}$, for $n > 1$.

lattice point   A point whose coordinates are integers.

Law of Cosines   Let a, b, and c denote the lengths of the sides of a given triangle, with angle A opposite the side with length a. Then we have the equality

$$a^2 = b^2 + c^2 - 2bc \cos A.$$

Law of Sines   Using the same notation as in the previous definition, we have equalities

$$\frac{a}{\sin A} = \frac{b}{\sin B} = \frac{c}{\sin C} = 2R,$$

where R is the radius of the circumcircle.

$\log x$ The logarithm of x to the base 10.

$\log_b x$ The logarithm of x to the base b.

Lucas number   A member of the sequence 2, 1, 3, 4, 7,..., where each number is the sum of the previous two numbers.

$\max\{a, b, \ldots\}$ The largest number in the set $\{a, b, \ldots\}$.

$\min\{a, b, \ldots\}$ The smallest number in the set $\{a, b, \ldots\}$.

natural number   An integer greater than 0.

NYSML   New York State Mathematics League.

${}_nP_r$ The number of permutations of n things taken r at a time; equal to $n!/(n - r)!$.

palindrome   A positive integer that reads the same forward and backward.

Pick's Theorem   See ARML 1994 Power Question.

pigeonhole principle   If N objects are distributed among $k < N$ boxes, some box contains at least two objects.

prime   A positive integer larger than 1 with no divisors other than 1 and itself.

proper divisor   A proper divisor of an integer is a divisor that is smaller than the integer itself.

Ptolemy's Theorem   A convex quadrilateral is cyclic if and only if the product of its diagonals equals the sum of the products of the two pairs of opposite sides.

relatively prime   Two positive integers a and b are relatively prime if $\gcd(a, b) = 1$.

TNYWR   The number you will receive. (Used in Relay Round.)

unit fraction   A fraction of the form $1/n$ where n is a positive integer.

INDEX

Index

Within each category, problems are listed according to competition (ARML or NYSML); year; type (Team, Individual, or Relay); number. Tiebreakers are listed as TB# (see section on Tiebreakers). For example, "A92T4" refers to ARML 1992, Team Question #4. Classification is generally by topic, rather than by method of solution, and some problems are listed under more than one category.

Algebra

Binomial expansion (*see also* **Combinatorics**): A93I6, A94T1
Complex numbers: N91T9, A91T8, A92T8, A92R1-2, A94I6, TB1
Equations, solving (*see also* Theory of Equations):
  absolute value: A91T5, N92T7
  cubic: N92T10
  integer (*see also* **Number Theory**: Diophantine equations): A89T1, A89I1, A92I1, A93I1
  polynomial of degree four or more: A89I3
  quadratic: N91I2, A91R2-1, N92I7, N92R1-3, A92T4, TB13, TB23
  radical: A89R1-1
  systems (of): N89I4, N90I2, N90I3, N91I6, A91I1
  miscellaneous: N90T1, A90I7, A91T4, A93I7
Extreme values (maximum-minimum problems): A90I3, A90I7, TB5
Factorization of polynomials: N89I2
Functions and functional relations: N91T6, A94T9
Greatest integer function: A89I6, A90R1-3, N91R2-1, A91I5, A94I3, TB7
Inequalities: A89R2-1, A90I2
Limits: N89T2

Logarithms: A89R2-2, N90T3, A90I5, A91R1-2, N92R1-1, A92R2-2, A93R2-1, TB5, TB16, TB19
Means: A93T8, A93I3
Recursion and iteration: A92R2-3
Sequences and series:
  arithmetic: N89I5, A91I3, N92T9, N92I6, TB24
  geometric: A94I8
  miscellaneous: N89T8, N89I5, N90T6, A90T9, A91T7, A92I4, A94R1-3, TB6, TB9
Miscellaneous topics:
  arithmetical or computational: N89R1-1, A89T2, N90T4, N90R1-1, A90T1, A90I1, A90R1-2, A90R2-2, N91I3, A91T2, A92I2, A92T7, A93T1, A93R1-1, A93R1-2, A94I5, A94R1-1
  assorted algebraic techniques: N89T7, A89T6, N90I8, A90T7, A91I2, N92I3, N92R2-2, N92R2-3, A93I6, A93R2-3, A94R1-2, A94R2-1, TB3, TB21
  various word problems: N89R2-4, A90T4, N91T3, A94T7, A94I8

Analytic Geometry

Lattice points: A91R2-3, A92I5, TB22
Problems, involving conics: N89T3, N91T1, A92T2, A94T6, A94I7, A94R2-3, TB26

187

Colophon

This book was typeset in Lucida, a new type family designed by Charles Bigelow and Kris Holmes specifically for scientific publishing. The Lucida type family includes a set of serif faces, sans serif faces, and mathematical fonts, covering the entire range of type required for book composition. The letterforms have large x-heights and open interiors that enhance legibility with modern printing technology.

This book was composed using LaTeX 2.09, a macro package built on the TeX typesetting system created by Donald E. Knuth.

The paper is Plainfield Opaque, an acid-free paper that will extend the life of the book.

Composition and Art: Techsetters, Inc., Cherry Hill, NJ
Copyediting: Stanley Rabinowitz, MathPro Press, Westford, MA
Cover: Kathi Duprey, Ad Infinitum Graphic Services, Ayer, MA
Fonts: Y&Y, Carlisle, MA
Indexing: Larry Zimmerman and Gil Kessler
Printing: BookMasters, Mansfield, OH